Quick and Simple Chair Exercises For Seniors

10-Minute Workouts to Improve Your Agility and Maintain Your Independence, Including Essential Health Tips for Holistic Living and Everyday Vitality

Audrey Fitzgerald

~Dedications~

To all of my wonderful friends who supported me on this amazing journey,
I feel so very blessed and grateful to have found people like you!

If you like this book, please check out this other book from the same author:

Quick and Simple Chair Yoga for Seniors Over 60: The Fully Illustrated Guide to Seated Poses and Cardio Exercises for Weight Loss and Mobility to Maintain Your Independence in Under 10 Minutes a Day!

https://a.co/d/88wdUd9

Table of Contents

INTRODUCTION 1

CHAPTER ONE:
WHY CHAIR EXERCISES FOR SENIORS? 4

    The Advantages of Chair Exercises for Seniors 5
    The Benefits of Walking 8

CHAPTER TWO:
AGING GRACEFULLY, ONE HABIT AT A TIME 11

    The Process of Habit Formation 11
    Habit Stacking 14
    Habit Cues 17
    Types of Habit Cues 17
    Habit Monitoring 20
    Habit Scheduling 23
    Habit Accountability 25
    Habit Convenience 27
    How to Break Bad Habits and Create Positive Ones 29
    The Role of Consistency in Achieving Results 32

CHAPTER THREE:
10-MINUTE SEATED MOBILITY EXERCISES: MAINTAINING FLEXIBILITY AND UPPER BODY
FUNCTIONALITY 34

    Start with 3–10 Deep Breaths 36
    Shrug Shoulders Up/Down 38
    Pull Shoulders Back 40
    Shoulder Cross-Arm Stretch 42
    Back of Arm Triceps Stretch 44
    Seated Calf Stretch Pose 46
    Seated Elbow Circles 48
    Seated Cactus Arms Flow 50
    Chair Torso Circles 52
    Seated Hand Clenches 54
    End with 3–10 Deep Breaths 56

CHAPTER FOUR:
IMPROVING BALANCE: CHAIR EXERCISES TO ENHANCE STABILITY IN JUST 10 MINUTES 59

    Start with 3–10 Deep Breaths 60
    Tree Pose with Chair 62
    Downward-Facing Dog Pose Variation with Chair 64
    Chair Mountain Pose One Leg Backlift 66
    Shoulder Pendulum Exercise with Chair 68
    Dancer's Pose with Chair 70
    Half Wide Legged Forward Fold Pose with Chair 72
    End with 3–10 Deep Breaths 74

CHAPTER FIVE:
10-MINUTE STRENGTHENING AND TONING: CHAIR EXERCISES FOR LOWER BODY STRENGTH 77

Start with 3–10 Deep Breaths 78
Heel Raises with Chair 80
Hip Abduction with Chair..82
Hip Extension Leg Lift with Chair 84
Flamingo Swing with Chair 86
Hamstring Curl with Chair 88
End with 3–10 Deep Breaths..90

CHAPTER SIX:
MINDFUL EATING: A KEY TO HEALTHY AGING **94**

Phytonutrients and Their Benefits..95
Phytonutrients: Eat the Rainbow!...99
Eating Well, Aging Better: Introduction to the Paleo Diet 101
The Quick and Simple Power Paleo Meal Plan 109
Power Paleo Meal Suggestions 117

CHAPTER SEVEN:
PUTTING IT ALL TOGETHER: A HOLISTIC APPROACH TO AGING WELL **119**

Supplements and Vitamins for Healthy Aging 120
How to Choose Quality Supplements 123
Incorporating Chair Exercises into Daily Life 126
Incorporating Wellness Practices into Daily Life..129
Embracing the Process and Enjoying the Journey 136

CONCLUSION **140**

REFERENCES..**142**

Introduction

You wake up one morning, ready to tackle the day, but as you try to rise from your bed, you feel stiff and achy. You think to yourself, "How on earth did it get this way?" You remember your once vibrant spirit, and you long for the energy you had before and wonder what can be done about it.

But fear not. You're not alone. Neither should you despair, for I have something that can help you regain control of your life, boost your vitality, and celebrate the beauty of aging with open arms.

Aging comes with wisdom, experience, and a deep appreciation for the little joys in life. It's time to let go of negative societal views on aging and embrace the self-respect and admiration that come with being an elder!

As we age, maintaining a healthy and active lifestyle becomes increasingly important for our overall well-being. Physical activity is essential for promoting a healthy aging process and can play a significant role in averting or delaying various health issues that you may encounter as you grow older.

Regular exercise is a key component of a healthy lifestyle, helping to improve strength, flexibility, balance, and cardiovascular health. However, for seniors and people with limited mobility or physical challenges, traditional exercise routines like heavy weightlifting and high-intensity cardio may seem daunting or even impossible to perform. That's where chair exercises come in. Chair exercises provide a safe and accessible workout option!

The beauty of chair exercises lies in their versatility and adaptability. They can be modified to suit different fitness levels and abilities, allowing seniors to gradually progress at their own pace. Whether you're needing to take it slower temporarily, or simply looking to start getting active, chair exercises offer a wide range of benefits for older adults.

This book was born out of a deep understanding of where you are in life and what you need. I've seen the challenges you experience—both physical and emotional—and I am here to support you on your journey to a healthier and happier life! For the past two decades, I have been actively involved in guiding my mother through movement routines and offering dietary advice, witnessing firsthand the numerous benefits she has experienced from both.

My passion for health and well-being dates back to my teenage years, and in 1996, I pursued professional chef training. During this time, I started incorporating healthier alternatives into the recipes I learned, leading to the establishment of a natural foods personal chef and catering company with a strong focus on overall client wellness.

In 2001, I delved into alignment-based yoga and became a teacher of yoga, meditation, and movement, including chair exercises and chair yoga. This journey eventually led me to establish a wellness lifestyle coaching company that adopted a holistic approach to well-being, encompassing the body, mind, and spirit. Even after two decades, my enthusiasm for sharing movement and nutritional advice with loved ones remains unwavering.

My mother recently celebrated her 81st birthday, and as of now, she plays ping pong and does Zumba regularly, delighting in the combination of physical movement and enjoyable social interaction. When I was in my late twenties, I began teaching her chair yoga and exercises when she was in her early sixties, providing her with poses she could practice independently.

Although it was initially challenging for her, I shared useful tips and information similar to the content that I have included in this book, and everything gradually fell into place. I genuinely believe that the consistent movement she has maintained over the past 20 years significantly contributes to her ability to engage in Zumba and ping pong at the age of 81. Having said that, I believe anyone can start at any age. It is my sincere wish for all seniors to experience such vitality, which is why I am writing this book!

I grew up in Hawaii, where elders are revered, as they are in many indigenous cultures. *Kupuna* means "honored elder" in Hawaiian, and we treat our elders with respect and admiration. I believe all people should look at themselves this way as they become elders in their community!

This guide offers simple, effective chair exercises tailored specifically for seniors, as well as nutritional guidance and the keys to cultivating a vibrant and healthy lifestyle. Within these pages, you will find the tools to reshape your perspective, reclaim your vitality, and lead a life that celebrates the richness of experience that comes with age. I regard it as important to help you out by providing you with a road map to a healthier, happier, and fulfilled life. I designed this book to be a body, mind, and spirit wellness guide as I believe it's all connected, and success in one area helps all the other areas to be successful as well!

Are you ready to say "goodbye" to all your frustrations, struggles, pain, and fear of losing independence as you age? If "yes," keep reading!

Chapter One:
Why Chair Exercises for Seniors?

Joan MacDonald, an 82-year-old fitness fanatic, is living proof that age is never a limiting factor if you want to make big life changes. At the age of 70, Joan found herself overweight, on multiple medications to manage her condition, and struggling with her mobility. Determined to take control of her health, she embarked on a remarkable fitness journey that completely changed her life. Through consistent exercise and a balanced diet, Joan shed excess pounds, built strength and endurance, and regained her vitality.

Now in her 80s, Joan continues to prioritize her fitness and well-being. She attends regular workout sessions, takes part in fitness challenges, and consistently pushes herself to new limits. Her story serves as a reminder that it's never too late to start or restart a fitness journey.

Joan MacDonald's fitness success story is a powerful example of resilience, determination, and the transformative power of a healthy lifestyle. Her story inspires people of all ages to take charge of their health, break free from limitations, and live their best lives at any stage of life.

Inspired by Joan's incredible success, this chapter delves into the importance of maintaining mobility and flexibility as we age and highlights the significance of staying physically active and maintaining independence for seniors. Within this chapter, you will discover the advantages of chair exercises for seniors and the benefits of walking, a low-impact exercise that can be added as an option to your physical fitness regimen.

I realize that some people have come to this book with less mobility and are not as agile to consider walking. But I just want to offer it as something wonderful to be paired with the chair exercises and something to shoot for if that's a possibility in your future.

By adopting the principles outlined in this chapter, seniors can embrace their golden years with vitality, independence, and a renewed sense of purpose. The remarkable story of Joan MacDonald serves as a testament to the transformative power of fitness and making good choices, proving that age is just a number when it comes to achieving optimal health and well-being.

The Advantages of Chair Exercises for Seniors

As we age, maintaining a physically active lifestyle becomes increasingly important for our overall health and well-being. For seniors who may face mobility limitations or balance issues, chair exercises offer a safe and effective way to stay active. These exercises, specifically designed to be performed while using a chair, provide numerous advantages that contribute to maintaining strength, flexibility, cardiovascular health, mental well-being, and overall quality of life. This section explores the benefits of chair exercises for seniors and highlights why incorporating them into a daily routine can lead to a healthier and more fulfilling life.

- *Accessibility and Safety:* One of the primary advantages of chair exercises for seniors is their accessibility and safety. Seniors with mobility limitations or balance issues can safely engage in chair exercises. This accessibility makes chair exercises suitable for a wide range of individuals, regardless of their physical condition.

- *Improved Strength and Muscle Tone:* Regular engagement in chair exercises allows seniors to maintain and improve their strength and muscle tone. These exercises target various muscle groups, including the arms, legs, core, and back. By incorporating resistance movements and gentle weight-bearing exercises, seniors can enhance their overall body strength and stability. Strong muscles not only improve mobility and balance but also aid in performing daily activities independently, thus promoting a sense of confidence and self-sufficiency.

- *Enhanced Flexibility and Range of Motion:* As we age, joint stiffness and reduced flexibility can become common issues. Chair exercises provide an effective means to combat these challenges by incorporating gentle stretches and movements that help improve flexibility and increase range of motion. Regular exercise can alleviate joint stiffness, reduce the risk of muscle imbalances, and promote better mobility. Seniors who engage in chair exercises often experience increased comfort in their daily activities, such as reaching for objects or bending down to tie their shoes.

- *Increase Coordination:* Incorporating repetitive and structured exercises into seniors' routines can help build muscle memory, allowing them to preserve hand-eye coordination and prolong their independence.

- *Improved Cardiovascular Health:* Maintaining cardiovascular health is crucial for seniors and chair exercises can contribute to achieving this goal. Engaging in exercises that elevate the heart rate, such as the exercise in Chapter Five, helps seniors maintain their cardiovascular fitness. Regular cardiovascular activity improves heart health, enhances circulation, and boosts overall stamina (Pinckard et al., 2019). It also improves endurance for daily activities, leading to an improved quality of life (Pinckard et al., 2019).

- *Weight Management:* Chair exercises can play a significant role in weight management for seniors. Regular physical activity, even while seated, burns calories and increases metabolism. By incorporating chair exercises into their routine, seniors can achieve and maintain a healthy weight. Moreover, maintaining a healthy weight can contribute to improved energy levels, a better mood, and increased overall self-esteem.

- *Improved Posture and Balance:* Chair exercises that focus on strengthening the core, back, and leg muscles—like the ones in Chapter Five—can help seniors maintain good posture and improve balance. Engaging in exercises that target these muscle groups enhances the support and stability needed for maintaining an upright posture. By promoting better posture and balance, chair exercises allow seniors to maintain their independence and overall physical well-being.

- *Improved Overall Mental Well-being:* Physical activity has a profound impact on mental health, and chair exercises are no exception. When we exercise regularly, our body releases endorphins, the "feel-good" hormones, which elevate mood and enhance cognitive function. Engaging in chair exercises provides a sense of accomplishment, promotes relaxation, and reduces stress levels. Moreover, participating in chair exercise classes or group activities offers opportunities for social interaction and community engagement. The combination of physical and social engagement can contribute to a positive mental outlook and overall well-being.

In general, regular movement contributes to decreased pain levels. Extended periods of sedentary behavior are not natural for the human body. However, it is important to consider individual circumstances. If recovering from anything or dealing with a condition impacting muscles or joints, it is important to consult with a doctor regarding an appropriate exercise regimen. Always follow the advice of healthcare professionals or physical therapists regarding the frequency and intensity of exercise. Chair exercises can also help alleviate certain types of pain when done properly.

The Benefits of Walking

Just put one foot in front of the other, and before you realize it, you could be walking your way to better health! Walking is a simple yet powerful form of exercise that holds numerous benefits for people of all ages. But, for seniors, walking is even more advantageous as it offers a low-impact and accessible way to stay physically active. If you do have the mobility for even just a short walk regularly or can work up to this in the future, it is a very good idea to add walking to your fitness regimen.

Engaging in regular, brisk walking has been shown to help older adults with the following:

- *Improve Cardiovascular Health:* Walking is a great cardiovascular exercise that helps seniors maintain and improve their heart health. Regular walking routines elevate the heart rate, strengthening the heart and improving its efficiency. Studies have repeatedly indicated that regular walking can help improve circulation and decrease blood pressure (Omura et al., 2019; Murtagh et al., 2010). Prominent studies conducted at the University of Colorado at Boulder and the University of Tennessee revealed that engaging in a daily walking routine, covering a few miles, contributed to the reduction of blood pressure among elderly women (McGinn et al., 2008).

- *Improve Bone Health and Strength:* Although walking is a fairly low-impact form of exercise, it is still a whole-body workout, which benefits your muscles and bones. Walking puts a healthy amount of stress on the bones, promoting bone density and strength. Additionally, walking outdoors exposes seniors to natural sunlight, which allows their bodies to produce vitamin D, a vital nutrient for bone health. By walking regularly, seniors can maintain strong bones and maintain independence in their daily activities.

- *Improve Sleep Habits:* If you take a walk in the early morning, you may find it easier to catch a few "Z's" at night! Researchers focused on women aged 50 to 75 and found that those who engaged in regular morning walks slept much better compared to those who did not partake in walking activities (Mc Tiernan et al., 2003).

- *Enhance Joint Health and Mobility:* Walking helps lubricate the joints and maintain mobility. Walking also strengthens the muscles surrounding the joints, providing them with better support and stability. By maintaining joint health and mobility through walking, seniors can continue to perform daily living activities with ease, enhancing their overall quality of life.

- *Support Healthy Weight Management:* Maintaining a healthy weight is crucial for seniors to prevent various health issues. Walking is an effective way to manage weight, as it burns calories and boosts metabolism. Regular walking routines help seniors maintain a healthy body weight or achieve weight loss goals. Moreover, walking stimulates muscle growth, which helps to increase metabolic rate even at rest. Similarly, different studies have indicated that maintaining a regular walking routine can assist in curbing one's desire for sugary treats, resulting in reduced cravings (Leow et al., 2018; Ledochowski et al., 2015).

- *Promotes Mental Well-being:* Walking has significant benefits for mental health, which is particularly important for seniors. Regular physical activity, such as walking, releases endorphins, the "feel-good" hormones, which elevate mood and promote a sense of well-being. Walking outdoors also provides exposure to nature, fresh air, and sunlight, which can improve mental clarity and boost overall mood. Additionally, walking can be a social activity, allowing seniors to socialize with friends, neighbors, or walking groups. Walking's positive impact on mental well-being enhances the overall quality of life for seniors. Several studies have repeatedly showcased the immense benefits of maintaining social connections for the mental and physical well-being of older individuals (Asante & Karikari, 2022; Newman & Zainal, 2020).

- *Improve Balance:* Walking is an excellent way to improve balance. It strengthens the muscles in the legs and core, which are essential for stability. Walking also enhances coordination and proprioception, the body's awareness of its position in space. Regular walking promotes better balance overall.

Your well-being and happiness are not about living perfectly. It is all about making good choices and finding new ways to stay active. The good news is that it's never too late to start making better choices for a more fulfilling life. Age is just a number when it comes to staying fit and happy. Get moving, and you will move toward a healthier and happier life!

Chapter Two:
Aging Gracefully, One Habit at a Time

Habits are an integral part of our daily lives, shaping our behaviors and influencing our long-term outcomes. Whether it's the morning ritual of brushing our teeth or the automatic act of reaching for a snack when we're stressed, habits play a significant role in our routines. But have you ever wondered how habits form and why they are so difficult to break? The answer lies in the intricate workings of our brain and the science of habit formation.

The Process of Habit Formation

Every habit starts with a psychological pattern called a "habit loop," which is a three-step process that occurs within our brain. First, there's a cue, a trigger, which tells our brain to enter automatic mode and let a particular behavior unfold. Next comes the routine, which can be a physical, mental, or emotional action—in simple terms, the behavior itself. Finally, there is the reward—something that your brain likes that helps it remember the "habit loop" in the future. As this cycle repeats—cue, routine, reward; cue, routine, reward—it becomes increasingly automatic. The cue and reward become closely linked, leading to a strong sense of anticipation and craving. Eventually, a habit is formed.

One of the fundamental concepts underlying habit formation is "chunking." Our brains naturally seek patterns and ways to simplify complex tasks. When we repeatedly perform a sequence of actions, our brain combines them into a single unit called a chunk. For example, when learning to drive, we initially focus on each action: adjusting the mirrors, pressing the pedals, and steering. However, with practice, these actions become automatic, forming a chunk of behavior. Chunking allows our brains to conserve cognitive resources, making it easier and faster to execute familiar tasks.

Consistency is key when it comes to forming and maintaining habits. Research has shown that repetition is essential for rewiring the neural pathways in our brains (Zhan et al., 2018). Each time we perform a behavior, a signal is sent through a specific neural pathway. The more frequently we engage in the behavior, the stronger and more efficient the neural connection becomes. Over time, this repetition establishes a default pattern, making the behavior automatic.

The duration required to form a habit varies depending on the complexity of the behavior and individual factors. Studies suggest that habits can take anywhere from a few weeks to several months to become ingrained (Lally et al., 2009). It is important to be patient during the habit formation process and not become discouraged if immediate results are not apparent.

To increase the likelihood of a habit sticking, it needs to align with our values and goals. When our habits are in harmony with our core values, they become a reflection of who we are, reinforcing our motivation to maintain them. For example, if fitness is an important value, incorporating regular exercise into our daily routine aligns with that value and increases the chances of forming a lasting habit.

Environmental cues also play a significant role in triggering habit-related behavior. Our surroundings provide contextual cues that activate specific neural pathways associated with a habit. For instance, entering a gym can trigger the habit of working out. By manipulating our environment to create cues that support desired behaviors, we can increase the likelihood of habit formation. Placing workout clothes near the bed or keeping healthy snacks readily available can serve as reminders and facilitate the desired habits.

Breaking larger habits into smaller, manageable steps is an effective strategy to increase success rates. The daunting nature of a big goal can be overwhelming and demotivating. By dividing the habit into smaller actions, each step becomes more achievable, building momentum and fostering a sense of accomplishment. This approach allows us to focus on the process rather than the outcome, making habit formation a more manageable and sustainable endeavor.

Positive reinforcement and rewards are powerful tools in habit formation. Our brains are wired to seek pleasure and avoid pain. By associating positive experiences with the desired behavior, we create a feedback loop that reinforces the habit. This can be as simple as giving yourself a small reward after completing a task or celebrating milestones along the way. These positive reinforcements not only strengthen the neural pathways associated with the habit but also enhance motivation and overall satisfaction.

Emotions and mindset significantly influence the formation and sustainability of habits. Positive emotions, such as enthusiasm and joy, can strengthen the habit-formation process, while negative emotions, like stress or self-doubt, can hinder progress. Cultivating a positive mindset, practicing self-compassion, and focusing on the benefits of the desired habit can create a conducive environment for successful habit formation.

Repetition and practice are fundamental to solidifying habits. The more we engage in a behavior, the more automatic it becomes. Consistency and perseverance are key, even when it feels challenging or monotonous. By repeatedly practicing the desired habit, we strengthen the neural connections associated with it, making it easier and more natural to perform over time.

Changing or replacing existing habits requires awareness and deliberate effort. It is essential to recognize the cues, routines, and rewards that drive the current habit and consciously intervene to establish new patterns. This process involves identifying triggers, developing alternative behaviors, and consistently practicing the new habit until it replaces the old one. With mindfulness and persistence, existing habits can be rewired to align with our goals and values.

Understanding the science behind habits empowers us to make intentional changes in our lives. By leveraging this knowledge, we can develop positive habits that align with our values and goals, ultimately leading to personal growth and fulfillment.

Habits are the building blocks of our daily lives, influencing our actions, behaviors, and overall well-being. When it comes to cultivating good habits like regular exercise and a healthy diet, understanding the science of habit formation can be a game-changer.

Habit Stacking

Habit stacking is a technique where you form new habits by linking a new desired behavioral change with an existing routine action you regularly perform, such as making coffee, brushing your teeth, or showering—or something that routinely happens in your day. It offers a powerful technique for seamlessly integrating new behaviors into our existing routines.

Habit stacking starts by recognizing the routines we already have in place. These routines act as a launching pad for introducing new habits. For instance, if we have the habit of brushing our teeth every morning, we can use that existing routine as a cue to incorporate a short workout session or a nutritious breakfast.

One of the key benefits of habit stacking is its ability to simplify behavior change. By building on familiar actions, we reduce the cognitive load associated with adopting new habits. This simplification enables us to focus our mental energy on the specific habit we want to cultivate. For example, if we aim to establish a regular exercise routine, we can anchor it to a daily habit like returning home from our day. This simple association makes it easier to overcome resistance and initiate the desired behavior.

Habit stacking also creates efficiency by saving time and mental energy. Instead of approaching each habit as an isolated task, stacking habits allows us to perform multiple actions in a single sequence. For instance, combining exercise with a healthy meal can be accomplished by scheduling a workout session immediately before meal preparation. This integrated approach reduces the need for separate blocks of time, allowing us to accomplish more in less time and with greater ease.

By anchoring new habits to established ones, habit stacking increases the likelihood of consistency and success. When we associate a desired behavior with an existing routine, we create a strong link in our minds. For instance, connecting a daily walk with drinking a morning cup of coffee ensures that the walk becomes an automatic response to the coffee cue. This association fosters consistency and helps us overcome the initial hurdles of habit formation.

Habit stacking leverages the power of associations to promote automaticity. Our brains naturally link activities together, and by consciously harnessing this process, we can establish positive habits more effectively. For example, if we want to incorporate chair exercises into our daily routine, we can associate it with the act of changing into workout attire. This pairing creates a mental link that facilitates the automatic execution of the desired behavior.

Linking habits through stacking creates a chain of positive actions that promote productivity. By aligning small habits with larger ones, we can build momentum gradually. For example, starting the day with a short meditation session can be followed by a healthy breakfast and a workout. Each habit reinforces the next, creating a virtuous cycle of productivity and positive actions.

Habit stacking strengthens the formation of desired behaviors over time. By consistently linking habits, we reinforce neural pathways in the brain associated with those behaviors. This repetition enhances the habit's stability and durability, making it more likely to stick in the long run. For example, combining a daily yoga practice with a post-work shower establishes a strong connection between the two, making the yoga habit more resilient to disruptions.

Habit stacking improves adherence by providing clear cues and sequential actions. When habits are linked in a specific order, it becomes easier to remember and follow through with the intended behaviors. By mapping out a clear sequence of actions, we remove ambiguity and reduce the likelihood of forgetting or skipping steps. This structured approach enhances adherence and minimizes the chances of falling off track.

Stacking habits fosters a sense of accomplishment and motivation. As we complete each linked habit, we experience a sense of achievement that fuels our motivation to continue. Moreover, witnessing the positive impact of these habits on our overall well-being further strengthens our resolve to maintain them. This cycle of accomplishment and motivation becomes a powerful driving force for continued habit stacking and personal growth.

Linking habits through stacking supports the development of a comprehensive routine. By integrating various habits into a cohesive framework, we create a holistic approach to self-improvement. For example, combining regular exercise, a balanced diet, and sufficient sleep forms the foundation of a healthy lifestyle. Habit stacking allows us to seamlessly incorporate these habits into our daily lives, ensuring a well-rounded routine.

Perhaps the most significant benefit of habit stacking is its potential to create a ripple effect for positive life changes. As we successfully implement new habits and witness their transformative effects, we become more open to embracing additional positive behaviors. The momentum generated by habit stacking spills over into other areas of our lives, catalyzing a chain reaction of self-improvement and personal growth.

Habit stacking is a powerful technique that harnesses the existing routines in our lives to facilitate the adoption of new, positive habits. By building on familiar actions, linking habits, and creating efficiency, habit stacking simplifies behavior change and increases the likelihood of long-term adherence.

Habit Cues

At the heart of habit formation lies the concept of habit cues. These cues serve as the initial spark that triggers the start of a habit loop or behavior. Whether it's a conscious decision or an unconscious trigger, identifying and harnessing these cues is key to establishing positive habits.

Types of Habit Cues

Visual Cues: Visual cues can play a vital role in prompting habit execution. Using visual cues like a post-it note on the fridge or a calendar notification can serve as gentle reminders to engage in exercise or make healthy food choices. These visual cues act as powerful prompts, drawing attention to the desired behavior and increasing the likelihood of habit execution.

Time: Time-based cues, such as setting alarms or establishing a consistent schedule, can help seniors establish regular habit reminders. For instance, setting a specific time for exercise or mealtimes can create a predictable routine that prompts the desired behaviors. These cues provide a sense of structure and help seniors maintain consistency in their healthy habits.

Environmental Cues: Our environment plays a significant role in shaping our behavior. For seniors, creating an environment that supports healthy habits is crucial. For example, arranging exercise equipment in a visible and accessible location or stocking the kitchen with nutritious foods can act as environmental cues that nudge seniors toward making positive choices. By surrounding themselves with supportive cues, seniors can create an environment that fosters healthy habits.

Emotional Cues: Emotions can act as powerful cues that prompt habit activation. Stress, boredom, or even loneliness can trigger unhealthy habits or cravings. By recognizing these emotional cues, we can develop strategies to replace negative habits with healthier alternatives. Engaging in physical activity or seeking social interaction can serve as positive outlets for emotional cues, supporting you in making healthier choices.

Internal Cues: Internal cues, such as hunger or fatigue, can significantly influence habit activation. We should pay attention to these internal cues and use them as reminders to prioritize our health and well-being. For example, feeling hungry can prompt you to prepare a nutritious meal, while recognizing fatigue can remind you to engage in light exercise or prioritize rest. By staying attuned to our internal cues, we can proactively address our physical and emotional needs.

Social Cues: Habits can be cued by people or social situations. Social cues play a powerful role in shaping behavior, particularly for seniors. For instance, having a workout partner or attending a fitness class can act as cues that prompt exercise. Seniors can leverage these cues by seeking out supportive social circles, joining exercise classes, or participating in healthy cooking groups and other social activities that align with their health goals.

One of the remarkable aspects of habit cues is their ability to initiate automatic behavior. Once a habit is established, the presence of a cue can act as a signal for the brain to engage in the associated behavior without requiring significant conscious effort. We can take advantage of this automatic response by consistently pairing specific cues with their desired habits. Over time, this repetition strengthens the habit loop, making it easier to maintain healthy behaviors.

Consistency is a key factor in habit formation. By using consistent cues, you can reinforce the desired habits and reduce decision fatigue. When cues are reliable and consistently associated with a specific behavior, you are more likely to engage in the desired habit without hesitation or uncertainty. This consistency alleviates the burden of decision-making, making it easier for us to adhere to exercise and healthy diet routines.

The clarity and specificity of habit cues significantly impact their effectiveness. Seniors should strive to use clear and specific cues that leave no room for ambiguity. For example, rather than setting a vague goal of "exercising more," setting a specific cue, such as "walking for 10 minutes after breakfast," provides a clear instruction that increases the likelihood of habit execution. Clear cues provide seniors with a definitive starting point and facilitate habit initiation.

Lastly, developing awareness of habit cues is essential for anyone looking to change or modify their habits. By understanding the triggers that prompt undesirable behaviors, seniors can consciously replace those cues with healthier alternatives. This self-awareness empowers you to take control of your habits and make deliberate choices that contribute to your well-being.

Harnessing the power of habit cues is a valuable strategy for adopting and maintaining healthy habits. Whether through visual cues, time-based reminders, environmental cues, or emotional triggers, cues act as signals for behavior initiation and serve as powerful tools for creating sustainable habits.

Habit Monitoring

Habit monitoring involves the conscious tracking of one's actions and behaviors. It serves as a means to enhance self-awareness and gain a deeper understanding of one's habits and routines. For seniors, tracking habits related to exercise and diet can be especially impactful. Regular exercise and a balanced diet are vital for maintaining physical and mental well-being as we age.

By monitoring their exercise habits, seniors can assess their activity levels and progress over time. Tools such as fitness trackers or exercise journals can provide valuable insights into patterns and achievements. For instance, tracking the number of steps taken or the duration and intensity of workouts can reveal trends and indicate areas for improvement. This self-awareness empowers seniors to take control of their exercise routine and make necessary adjustments to ensure they are meeting their health goals.

Similarly, monitoring dietary habits allows seniors to track their food intake, identify patterns, and make informed choices. Tracking the types and quantities of food consumed can shed light on nutritional imbalances and help seniors maintain a healthy weight. Habit-tracking tools, such as mobile apps or handwritten journals, can be invaluable in this process. They provide a convenient and organized way to record meals, track calorie intake, or monitor specific dietary restrictions.

Accountability and motivation are key components of habit formation. When seniors monitor their exercise and diet habits, they develop a sense of responsibility toward their well-being. Regular tracking instills a level of accountability as seniors become aware of their progress and take ownership of their actions. Moreover, monitoring helps foster motivation by providing visual evidence of achievements and milestones. Celebrating small wins, like completing a certain number of workouts in a week or reaching a target weight, can boost morale and encourage seniors to continue their healthy habits.

Habit tracking tools offer a range of benefits to seniors. These tools facilitate the habit monitoring process, making it easier to track and analyze data. For example, mobile apps can provide reminders, offer personalized recommendations, and even generate reports that highlight progress or areas that require attention. On the other hand, traditional methods like handwritten journals allow for a more tactile and personal approach to habit tracking. Seniors can choose the method that best suits their preferences and needs, ensuring seamless integration into their daily routines.

By monitoring your habits consistently, you can identify barriers and adjust your strategies accordingly. Habits are often influenced by external factors, such as time constraints or environmental challenges. Regular monitoring enables you to recognize these barriers and find creative solutions. For instance, if you notice a lack of exercise on certain days due to a busy schedule, you can proactively plan shorter workouts or integrate physical activity into other parts of your day.

Moreover, habit monitoring encourages self-reflection and personal growth. Seniors can take moments to reflect on their habits, exploring their motivations, triggers, and emotional connections. This self-awareness can lead to deeper understanding and open avenues for personal development. By recognizing patterns or areas for improvement, seniors can refine their habits and make positive changes that contribute to their overall well-being.

Another advantage of habit monitoring is the ability to receive feedback and make necessary adjustments. When seniors track their exercise and diet habits, they gain insights into the correlations between their actions and desired outcomes. This feedback enables them to optimize their routines and modify their approach when needed. For instance, if a senior notices a lack of progress in weight loss despite consistent exercise, they can seek guidance from a healthcare professional to refine their dietary choices.

In addition to feedback, habit monitoring provides you with a visual representation of the consistency of your habits over time. Seeing progress and positive trends can be incredibly motivating and reassuring. Conversely, recognizing periods of inconsistency can serve as a wake-up call and a reminder to refocus on your health goals. This visual representation serves as a powerful tool for tracking your journey and adjusting your efforts accordingly.

Habit monitoring ultimately fosters a sense of control and empowerment. By actively tracking your habits, you take charge of your well-being and become an agent of change. You gain a deeper understanding of your body, your habits, and the impact of your choices. Real-time monitoring helps maintain focus and prevent habit regression, ensuring that you stay on track and continue your healthy behaviors.

Habit monitoring is a valuable tool for seniors striving to lead healthy and fulfilling lives. The ability to monitor habits consistently offers accountability, motivation, and opportunities for personal growth. Whether through the use of apps or handwritten journals, habit-tracking tools provide the means to celebrate milestones, receive feedback, and foster a sense of control. By embracing habit monitoring, seniors can pave the way for healthy aging and improve their overall well-being.

Habit Scheduling

At the heart of habit scheduling lies the notion of setting a specific time and day for habit execution. By allocating dedicated slots in our daily or weekly schedules, we create a framework that supports the formation of healthy routines. For instance, you can set aside 10 minutes each morning for a brisk walk or engage in light exercises in the afternoon. These designated times ensure that physical activity becomes an integral part of your life.

Time blocking, another essential strategy, involves allocating dedicated slots for habit implementation. This approach provides structure and helps seniors prioritize their health. By blocking out specific periods for exercise and meal preparation, they can ensure that these activities receive the attention they deserve. Seniors may choose to incorporate exercise sessions into their morning routine or schedule them during the least busy times of their day, ensuring they have the energy and focus necessary to engage in physical activity effectively.

Scheduling relevant habits enhances consistency and eliminates ambiguity in their formation. When we assign specific times for exercise and healthy meals, we eliminate any uncertainty and create a sense of commitment. Seniors can set reminders or alarms to prompt habit execution at the designated times, serving as gentle nudges to follow through with their intentions.

To ensure that habits are prioritized and completed, you can integrate them into your daily or weekly schedules. By acknowledging the importance of exercise and a healthy diet and allocating dedicated time for them, these activities are less likely to be neglected or postponed. Prioritizing habits sends a clear message that your well-being is a top concern, instilling a sense of self-care and self-worth.

Procrastination can often hinder the establishment of healthy habits, but habit scheduling can help overcome this challenge. By designating specific times for exercise and meal preparation, we eliminate the opportunity for procrastination to creep in. When the scheduled time arrives, it becomes a nonnegotiable commitment, fostering a proactive mindset and discouraging the temptation to postpone or skip these essential activities.

Flexibility is a key element of habit scheduling, allowing you to adapt to different routines or circumstances. Life can be unpredictable, and unexpected events may disrupt established schedules. However, by incorporating flexibility into your habit schedules, you can adjust and find alternative times or methods to engage in exercise or adhere to a healthy diet. This adaptability ensures that habits remain an integral part of your life, regardless of external factors.

Consistent habit scheduling establishes a rhythm and reinforces habit development. By adhering to a structured schedule, you create a sense of rhythm and familiarity, making habit execution feel natural and effortless. Over time, these consistent actions become ingrained in your daily life, leading to long-term habit formation. Whether it is the daily morning walk or the balanced meal consumed at noon, the consistent rhythm established through scheduling reinforces the development of healthy habits.

Creating a visual schedule or using digital tools can significantly aid habit adherence. You can benefit from creating a visual representation of your habit schedule, such as a wall calendar or a digital planner. This visual reminder serves as a powerful tool to reinforce your commitment and track your progress.

Habit scheduling enables seniors to balance multiple habits and priorities effectively. By allocating specific time slots for various activities, seniors can strike a harmonious balance between exercise, maintaining a healthy diet, and other commitments in their lives. This balanced approach ensures that their well-being remains a top priority without neglecting other essential aspects of their daily routines.

Habit Accountability

When it comes to forming healthy habits, accountability acts as a driving force in maintaining commitment and motivation. Sharing our goals and progress with others creates a sense of external accountability. Whether it's telling a friend or a family member or joining a community group, the act of sharing holds us responsible for our actions. This increased responsibility fuels our motivation, as we are less likely to abandon our efforts when others are aware of our objectives. The support and encouragement received from these accountability partners or groups further reinforce our commitment, pushing us to stay focused on our habits.

One effective method of promoting accountability is by publicly tracking our habits. By making our goals and progress visible to others, we introduce a layer of social accountability. This can be achieved through various means, such as sharing updates on social media platforms or participating in online communities. When we know that others are observing our actions, we are more inclined to adhere to our habits consistently. Moreover, the positive feedback and recognition we receive from our peers further motivate us to stay on track, enhancing our commitment and dedication to our health goals.

Maintaining accountability requires regular check-ins and progress reviews. These periodic evaluations allow us to assess our progress and identify areas where improvement is needed. Whether it's scheduling weekly meetings with an accountability partner or dedicating time for personal reflection, these check-ins serve as reminders of our goals and help us stay focused. Moreover, reviewing our progress allows us to celebrate milestones and track our growth, instilling a sense of achievement and reinforcing our commitment to the habits we are trying to form.

Accountability fosters a sense of responsibility and ownership over our habits. When we hold ourselves accountable for our actions, we acknowledge that we have the power to shape our behavior and overall well-being. By taking ownership, we become more invested in the success of our habits, recognizing that our choices directly impact our health and quality of life.

This heightened sense of responsibility compels us to prioritize our habits and reinforces the importance of consistency in maintaining healthy behaviors.

To reinforce accountability for habit adherence, setting consequences or rewards can be highly effective. When we establish a system that holds us accountable for our actions, such as a consequence for skipping a workout or a reward for consistently following a healthy diet, we create a tangible incentive for staying on track. The fear of facing negative consequences or the anticipation of rewarding ourselves acts as an additional motivator, strengthening our commitment to maintaining our habits. These measures ensure that we stay consistent and aligned with our health goals.

Accountability is not solely about perfection but also about resilience. Setbacks and lapses are natural parts of the habit-formation process. When we encounter obstacles, reflecting on these setbacks helps us reestablish accountability. By analyzing what went wrong and learning from our mistakes, we can adjust our approach and find strategies to overcome challenges. This process cultivates resilience and ensures that setbacks do not derail our progress. Embracing accountability in these moments allows us to bounce back, reinforce our commitment, and continue moving forward on our journey toward healthier habits.

Habit Convenience

What we do is greatly influenced by how convenient it is. Convenient habits are those that can be easily integrated into daily routines and environments. It is essential to choose exercises and dietary practices that align with your preferences—that you enjoy or find interesting and that fit naturally into your existing lifestyle. For example, taking a walk in a nearby park or engaging in chair exercises at home are convenient options that can be easily incorporated into your daily routine without requiring significant changes or disruptions.

One way to increase habit convenience is by removing barriers and simplifying steps. You can identify any obstacles or complexities that hinder your engagement in healthy habits and find ways to eliminate or simplify them. For instance, laying out exercise clothing and equipment the night before can eliminate the time and effort spent searching for them, making it more convenient to start an exercise session. Similarly, having pre-prepared ingredients or healthy snacks readily available in the kitchen can simplify the process of maintaining a nutritious diet.

You should ensure that you have easy access to the resources and tools required for your chosen habits. This may include having comfortable walking shoes or a chair readily available for exercise or keeping a stock of fresh fruits, vegetables, high-quality proteins, and healthy fats in the pantry for healthy meal preparation. By removing the barrier of inaccessibility, you can effortlessly engage in your chosen habits.

Designing environments to support habits is an effective way to reduce friction and promote consistency, making your habits convenient. We can create a physical space that encourages healthy habits. For example, setting up a dedicated exercise area with exercise equipment or creating a cozy corner for reading while enjoying a nutritious snack can make it more convenient and enjoyable to engage in these habits regularly. The environment should be conducive to the desired habits, inspiring you to effortlessly incorporate them into your daily life.

Time efficiency is a crucial aspect of habit convenience. We often have busy schedules, so making habits time-efficient becomes essential. Choosing exercises that can be completed in shorter durations, like the ones included in the next chapters, allows us to get a comprehensive workout in less time. Similarly, meal prepping, or batch cooking, can save time and make healthy eating more convenient throughout the week. By prioritizing time efficiency, you can overcome resistance and make your habits more manageable.

We all face numerous decisions throughout the day, and each decision requires mental energy. By making healthy habits convenient, you can reduce decision fatigue and conserve your mental resources for other important choices. For instance, having a set workout routine eliminates the need to decide which exercises to do each day, reducing mental strain and making it easier to follow through consistently.

Proximity to triggers and cues increases habit convenience and promptness. You can strategically place cues or reminders in your environment to prompt habit execution. For instance, placing the exercise chair near the living room or setting up a fruit bowl as a visual reminder on the kitchen counter can make it easier to initiate exercise or healthy snacking. Proximity to triggers and cues acts as a gentle nudge, increasing convenience and promptness in habit formation.

Developing systems or routines that support habit execution improves convenience. You can establish daily or weekly routines that incorporate your desired habits. For example, designating specific days for grocery shopping and meal planning or scheduling exercise sessions at the same time each day creates a structured framework that supports habit formation. By developing systems that streamline their healthy routines, seniors can enjoy the convenience of a well-established habit ecosystem.

How to Break Bad Habits and Create Positive Ones

The first step in breaking bad habits is to identify triggers and replace them with healthier alternatives. Seniors should examine the situations, emotions, or thoughts that lead to their negative behaviors. For example, if unhealthy snacking tends to occur while watching television, they can replace that habit with a healthier alternative, such as enjoying a piece of fruit or engaging in a relaxing activity like puzzles or reading. By identifying triggers and finding healthier substitutes, seniors can weaken the strength of bad habits.

Starting small and gradually increasing the difficulty of new habits is an effective approach to creating positive habits. We all should set realistic goals and focus on one habit change at a time. For instance, if your goal is to incorporate regular exercise into your routine, you can begin with short walks and gradually increase the duration over time. Starting small allows for a sense of accomplishment and builds confidence, leading to long-term success in habit formation.

Creating a clear action plan and setting specific goals is crucial for breaking bad habits and cultivating positive ones. Seniors should outline the steps they need to take and establish a timeline for their habit change. For example, if your goal is to consume more fruits and vegetables, you can create a meal plan and set a specific target for the number of servings you aim to eat each day. A clear action plan provides guidance and structure, increasing the likelihood of successfully adopting positive habits.

Positive reinforcement and rewards play a significant role in reinforcing positive habits. We all should acknowledge and celebrate their achievements along the way. For example, you can reward yourself with a small treat or engage in a favorite hobby after completing a week of consistent exercise or maintaining a healthy diet. Positive reinforcement strengthens the association between the desired behavior and the reward, making it more likely for the habit to stick.

Seeking support from others or joining a supportive community is invaluable when it comes to breaking bad habits and creating positive ones. We can enlist the support of family, friends, or health professionals who can provide encouragement, accountability, and guidance throughout the habit change process. Joining a supportive community or participating in group activities, such as exercise classes or healthy cooking workshops, can foster a sense of camaraderie and motivation. The support of others can make the journey of habit change more enjoyable and successful.

Practicing self-awareness and mindfulness is essential to overcoming bad habits. Seniors should pay attention to their thoughts, emotions, and behaviors. By recognizing negative self-talk and replacing it with positive affirmations and encouragement, seniors can shift their mindset and empower themselves to make positive choices.

Breaking bad habits involves replacing them with new, positive routines. Seniors should develop alternative behaviors that align with their health goals. For example, instead of reaching for sugary snacks, they can opt for a piece of fresh fruit or a handful of nuts. By consciously substituting negative behaviors with healthier choices, seniors can gradually break the cycle of bad habits and establish new, positive routines.

Keeping a habit journal can be a valuable tool for tracking progress and reflecting on challenges. Seniors can record their daily habits, noting successes, setbacks, and any triggers or obstacles encountered. This journaling practice provides valuable insights into patterns and offers an opportunity for self-reflection and learning. It also serves as a visual reminder of progress and can motivate you during difficult times.

Implementing environmental changes can make adopting positive habits easier. Seniors should modify their surroundings to support their desired behaviors. For instance, they can keep healthy snacks readily available, create a designated exercise space in their home, or remove unhealthy temptations from their living environment. Environmental changes reduce the friction associated with habit change and make it more convenient to adopt and sustain positive behaviors.

Persistence and commitment are key throughout the habit-changing process. We should anticipate setbacks and not be discouraged by them. Even if a bad habit resurfaces, it is crucial to remain focused and committed to the larger goal. We should view setbacks as learning opportunities and recommit to positive habits. By staying persistent and resilient, you can overcome challenges and continue making progress toward your health goals.

Celebrating milestones and successes is essential in the journey of habit change. We should recognize and reward ourselves when we reach important milestones or make significant progress. Whether it's treating yourself to a favorite activity or sharing your achievements with loved ones, celebrating milestones reinforces positive habits and motivates you to continue your pursuit of a healthier lifestyle.

The Role of Consistency in Achieving Results

Consistency is a powerful force that plays a crucial role in achieving positive results, especially for those of us seeking to improve our health and well-being. When it comes to establishing good habits, such as regular exercise and maintaining a healthy diet, consistency is the key to success.

Being consistent reinforces behavior change and strengthens new habit formation. By consistently engaging in desired behaviors, you create a positive feedback loop that reinforces the neural pathways associated with those actions. For example, when you consistently exercise or make healthy food choices, your brain undergoes rewiring, gradually replacing old habits with new ones. This rewiring is facilitated by the repetition and consistency of your actions, leading to the formation of stronger neural connections and increasing the likelihood of habit stickiness.

Regular practice and repetition build momentum and increase the likelihood of habit stickiness. Seniors who engage in regular exercise or adhere to a healthy diet establish a rhythm and momentum that propel them forward. Each consistent action reinforces the habit and builds on previous efforts, making it easier to maintain the behavior over time. Repetition strengthens the neural pathways associated with the habit, making it more automatic and ingrained in daily routines.

We may face resistance or challenges when attempting to adopt new habits. However, consistency acts as a powerful tool for overcoming these obstacles. By consistently engaging in the desired behavior, you develop a sense of commitment and dedication, allowing yourself to push through resistance and stay on track. Consistency helps you build self-discipline and strengthen your willpower, providing the necessary foundation for long-term habit success.

Consistency ensures the integration of new habits into daily routines. You can enhance the likelihood of habit formation by incorporating your desired habits into your existing daily routines. For instance, scheduling exercise sessions at the same time each day or allocating specific time slots for meal preparation and healthy eating promotes consistency and seamlessly integrates these activities into your life. By integrating habits into daily routines, you create a sense of stability and predictability, reducing decision fatigue and resistance.

Being consistent builds trust and confidence in the ability to break bad habits and form new ones. As you consistently practice new habits, you witness your progress and experience the positive outcomes associated with those behaviors. This builds a sense of trust and confidence in your ability to break bad habits and form new, healthier ones. Trusting the process and your capabilities provides you with the motivation and belief needed to maintain consistency in your journey toward a healthier lifestyle.

Consistency creates a positive feedback loop of progress and motivation. Each consistent action reinforces a sense of progress and achievement, which in turn motivates you to continue your efforts. For example, as you see improvements in your physical strength, endurance, or overall well-being due to consistent exercise, you are encouraged to maintain the habit. This positive feedback loop nurtures motivation, ensuring that you remain committed and persistent in your pursuit of health and happiness!

Being consistent establishes new neural pathways for lasting behavior change. When we consistently engage in positive behaviors, our brains adapt and establish new neural pathways that support lasting behavior change. With time and consistent practice, these new pathways become stronger, making the desired behaviors more automatic and natural. By establishing new neural pathways, consistency paves the way for lasting behavior change and promotes the integration of healthy habits into our lives.

Lastly, consistency prevents relapse by replacing old triggers with consistent positive actions. Individuals who consistently engage in healthy habits create a buffer against relapse. By replacing old triggers, such as stress or negative emotions, with consistent positive actions, you reduce the likelihood of falling back into old, unhealthy patterns. Consistency acts as a shield, protecting seniors from the pull of old habits and empowering them to embrace healthier alternatives.

By embracing consistency, seniors can navigate the path to health and happiness with unwavering determination and achieve the lasting results they desire.

Chapter Three:
10-Minute Seated Mobility Exercises: Maintaining Flexibility and Upper Body Functionality

As we age, maintaining flexibility and upper body functionality becomes increasingly crucial for ensuring a high quality of life. Our upper body muscle groups share the spotlight in strengthening our body and improving our posture. You don't need to hit the weight rack and go heavy or spend the rest of your life in the gym to enhance flexibility, mobility, and strength in your upper body muscles. All you need are simple chair exercises that work them. Whether you are an active individual looking to add variety to your workout routine or someone seeking to reclaim independence in daily activities, chair exercises offer an effective and convenient solution.

Throughout this chapter, we will guide you through a series of seated mobility exercises, offering step-by-step instructions and illustrations that make it easy for you to follow along. You will discover exercises that target different areas of the body, including the neck, shoulders, arms, back, hips, and legs, promoting flexibility and strength in each region. These exercises can be effortlessly integrated into your daily life, empowering you to take control of your physical health and vitality.

While chair exercises offer the safest and gentlest path to reaching your health and fitness objectives, it's essential to seek your doctor's advice and get the green light before starting this practice. Make sure to consult your doctor about the specific exercises you should include or avoid.

The overarching principle in any exercise routine is "listening" to one's body. Pay close attention to how your body responds to each movement and work within your comfort zone. While it is natural to experience some discomfort during stretches, you must avoid pushing yourself too hard or forcing positions that cause pain. Always work within a pain-free range of motion. Improvements happen gradually, and pushing beyond your limit can lead to strain or injury. As you continue practicing, you should notice increased mobility and reduced discomfort over time.

There are several ways to achieve the same objective. That's why you will find a couple of different variations of the poses that work the same muscles in this book. So always feel free to choose what you feel is easier for you or best suits your activity level and condition.

You are encouraged to customize the number of repetitions according to your fitness level. For beginners or those with limited mobility, it is advisable to start with a lower number of repetitions and gradually increase them as you become more comfortable with the movements. More experienced individuals can challenge themselves with higher repetitions.

At first, it might take you a little longer than 10 minutes to complete the routines as you're learning the poses and reading the instructions. Don't worry; it's all part of the journey! As you become more familiar with the routines and gain confidence in your practice, it might take you even less than 10 minutes. Do as little or as much as you want, depending on your schedule and how much time you have. If you have more time, you can perform all three routines together, and if you have less time, you could take one routine and just do a few poses.

Keep in mind that chair exercises don't require any fancy equipment. With just a few basic items, you can easily embark on your exercise journey! A chair and a timer are enough to get started. The chair must be stable and not slide or move during the exercise. Choose a chair that has a firm and nonslip base, ensuring it remains steady throughout the exercise routine. A stable chair enables you to perform the movements with confidence. Do not chairs with wheels or unstable structures during the exercises.

A timer is handy for timing the poses and exercises. Most cell phones come equipped with timer apps these days. Setting the timer ensures that each exercise is performed for a suitable duration, allowing muscles to be adequately stretched and joints to move through their full range of motion.

So, grab a stable chair, set your timer, and embark on a journey toward a more flexible, mobile, and healthier you. Let's begin!

Start with 3–10 Deep Breaths

Deep breathing is an effective way to reduce stress, increase oxygen flow, and prepare your body and mind for physical activity.

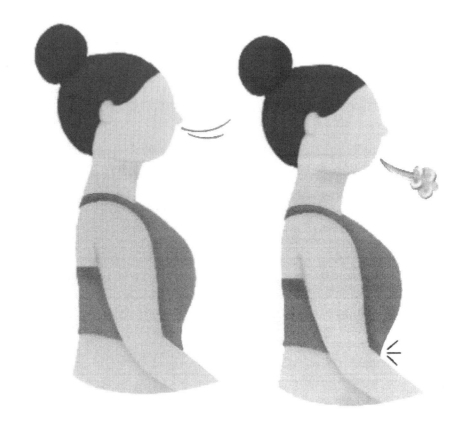

Step-by-Step Instructions:

- Sit up nice and tall in the chair, toward the edge, so that your back isn't leaning on the backrest of the chair. Keep your hands relaxing by your sides.

- Keep your back straight, spine lengthened, and feet flat and firmly planted on the floor, hip-width apart, with knees bent at a 90-degree angle.

- Place your hands on your thighs, palms facing downward.

- Keep your shoulders in a relaxed and neutral position, your chest raised, and allow your limbs and face to relax.

- Slightly engage your abdominal muscles, pulling your belly button toward your spine and slightly upward.

- Roll your shoulder blades down toward your back and let your elbows rest at your sides.

- Now close your eyes and inhale deeply through your nose, taking a slow and controlled breath in. Once you've taken a full breath in, hold it for a few seconds, but don't strain. Simply hold your breath comfortably.

- Exhale slowly and steadily through your mouth, allowing the air to escape at a controlled pace.

- Inhale deeply again, repeating the process for 3–10 complete breath cycles, depending on how much time you have.

- Once you've completed the breathing exercise, slowly and gently open your eyes and lower your hands down by your sides to return to the starting position.

Tip: During these deep breaths, try to clear your mind and focus solely on your breathing. This can be a form of mindfulness, helping you become more present and relaxed. After completing your deep breaths, you should feel more centered and relaxed.

Shrug Shoulders Up/Down

Most of us tend to hold a lot of tension in our shoulders. Shrugging our shoulders allows us to exaggerate the tension and then finally let it go fully. This exercise is ideal for relieving stress in the shoulders and quickly easing tension in both the body and mind. Moreover, it effectively lubricates the shoulder joints, increasing their mobility and strengthening the shoulder muscles.

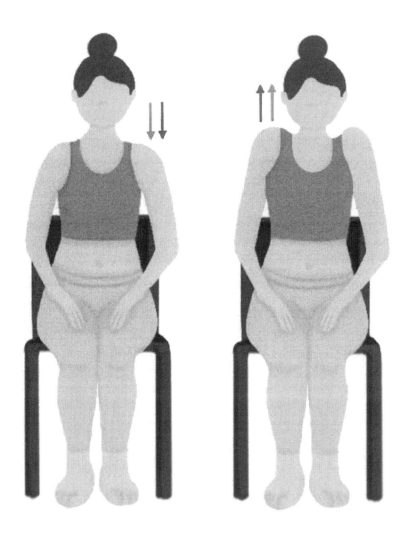

Step-by-Step Instructions:

- Sit on a chair with your feet flat on the floor and your back straight.

- Relax your arms by your sides, or keep your hands relaxed in your lap.

- Inhale deeply and slowly lift both shoulders toward your ears.

- Exhale and slowly lower your shoulders back down to the starting position.

- Repeat the exercise for 2 sets of 10 repetitions.

- You can take just one deep breath in between the sets or more if you need more time to rest.

- Focus on controlled and deliberate movements, avoiding any sudden jerks.

- Engage your core muscles to maintain stability and good posture.

Pull Shoulders Back

This exercise helps strengthen the scapula/shoulder blade muscles, which play a vital role in preventing your shoulders from slouching forward and enhancing your awareness of maintaining good posture.

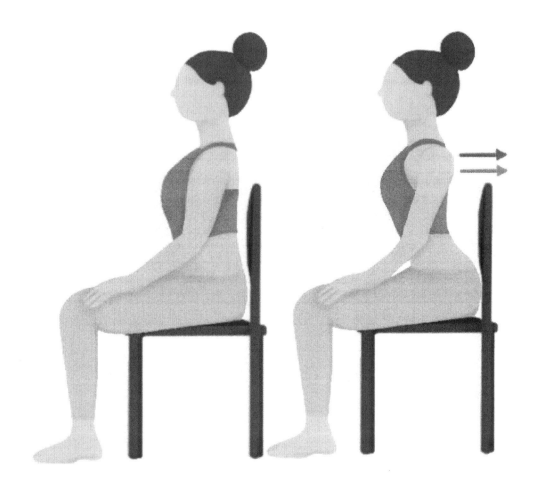

Step-by-Step Instructions:

- Sit on a chair with your back straight and your feet flat on the floor.

- Relax your arms by your sides, or keep your hands relaxed in your lap.

- Keep your chest lifted, and avoid slouching or rounding your shoulders forward.

- Inhale deeply, pull your shoulders back and gently squeeze your shoulder blades together.

- Hold for a count of 3 seconds, focusing on the contraction in your upper back muscles.

- Exhale and release the tension, allowing your shoulders to relax forward.

- Repeat the exercise for 2 sets of 10 repetitions.

- You can take just one deep breath in between the sets or more if you need more time to rest.

Shoulder Cross-Arm Stretch

The shoulder cross-arm stretch targets the rotator cuff muscles. It helps strengthen these muscles and provides a notable stretch in the posterior shoulders, increasing mobility in the shoulder joints.

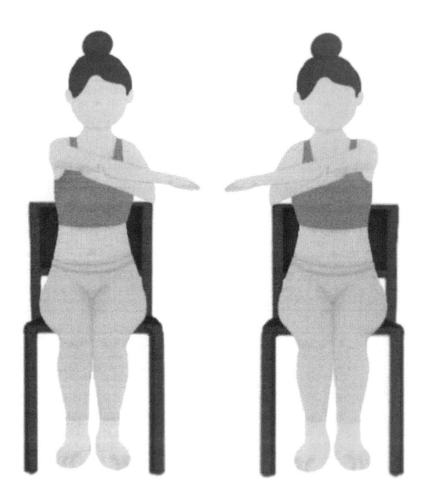

Step-by-Step Instructions:

- Sit on a chair with your back straight and your feet flat on the floor.

- Start with the arms relaxed by the sides.

- Inhale deeply and as you exhale, raise one arm straight in front of you, parallel to the floor.

- Reach that elbow across your chest toward the side.

- Hook your other arm around that elbow, gently applying pressure to deepen the stretch.

- Hold the stretch for 15–30 seconds, feeling the stretch in that shoulder and upper back.

- Keep your chest lifted and avoid slouching or leaning forward.

- Release the stretch, bringing that arm back to the starting position.

- Repeat the exercise on the opposite side.

Back of Arm Triceps Stretch

The back of arm triceps stretch enhances increased flexibility in the shoulder region, which is advantageous for activities that involve reaching up or behind.

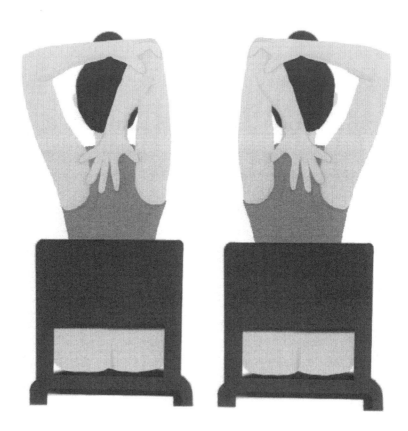

Step-by-Step Instructions:

- Sit on a chair with your back straight and your feet flat on the floor.

- Start with the arms relaxed by the sides.

- Extend one arm straight up toward the ceiling, keeping your palm facing inward.

- Bend that elbow and reach that hand toward the center of your upper back.

- Place your other hand on that elbow and gently apply pressure to deepen the stretch.

- Feel the stretch along the back of that arm (the triceps muscle).

- Keep your chest lifted and avoid slouching or leaning forward.

- Hold the stretch for 15–30 seconds, maintaining a comfortable level of tension.

- Continue to breathe deeply vand relax into the stretch.

- Release the stretch by bringing both hands down.

- Repeat the exercise on the opposite side.

Seated Calf Stretch Pose

A calf stretch helps stretch and strengthen the calf muscles, creating a range of motion in the ankle joints. This, in turn, enhances flexibility and mobility in the ankle joints, leading to improved balance and stability.

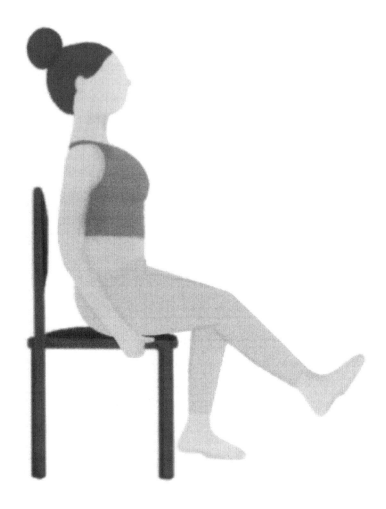

Step-by-Step Instructions:

- Sit on a chair with your back straight and your feet flat on the floor.

- Place your hands on the sides of the chair seat or your hips.

- Extend one leg forward, keeping your knee straight.

- Flex the foot of the extended leg by pulling your toes toward your body.

- Feel the stretch in your calf muscles and the back of your leg.

- Hold the flexed foot position for 15–30 seconds, maintaining a comfortable level of tension.

- Continue to breathe deeply and relax into the stretch.

- Release the stretch by relaxing your foot and returning it to a neutral position.

- Repeat the exercise on the opposite leg.

Seated Elbow Circles

This exercise works your arms and shoulders. It helps increase the range of motion in your shoulder joints as well as strengthen the shoulders and the arms, thus increasing the mobility and flexibility of the said muscles.

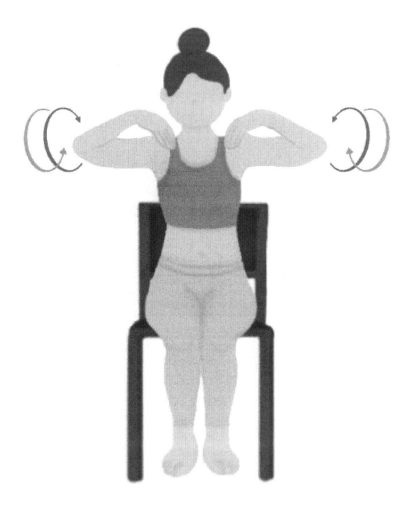

Step-by-Step Instructions:

- Sit on a chair with your back straight and your feet flat on the floor.

- Start with the arms relaxed by the sides.

- Inhale deeply and as you exhale, engage your core muscles for stability.

- Begin by stretching your arms out to the sides and bending the arms so that you're pointing your elbows out to the sides.

- Slowly roll your elbows along with your shoulders back in a circular motion.

- Perform the action for 10 shoulder circles.

- Focus on smooth and controlled movements, avoiding any sudden or jerky motions.

- Maintain good posture throughout the exercise, keeping your back straight.

- Adjust the size of the circles based on your comfort and range of motion.

- Then, reverse the direction of the circles.

Seated Cactus Arms Flow

This exercise helps strengthen your upper back, arms, and shoulders. The simple and gentle arm movements help open the chest, making this flow a gentle heart opener. Seated cactus arms flow helps boost energy in your entire body.

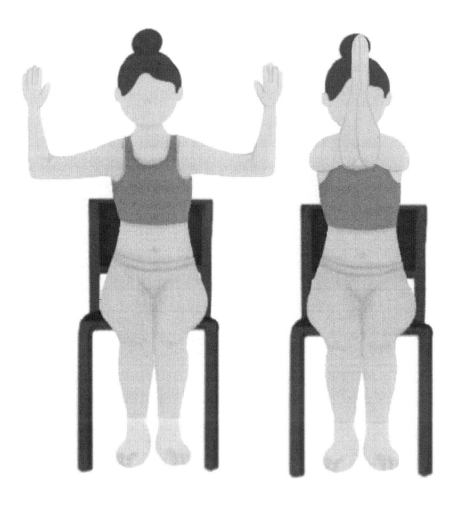

Step-by-Step Instructions:

- Sit on a chair with your back straight and your feet flat on the floor.

- Start with the arms relaxed by the sides.

- Inhale deeply and as you exhale, engage your core muscles for stability.

- Lift your arms to the sides, bending your elbows at 90-degree angles, resembling a cactus shape.

- Squeeze your shoulder blades together, open your chest, then inhale deeply.

- Exhale and slowly bring your forearms forward, pressing them together in front of your body.

- Inhale again and open your arms wide, returning to the starting cactus position.

- Repeat the flow by exhaling and pressing your forearms together in front of your body.

- Continue the flow, coordinating your breath with the movement of your arms.

- Repeat the exercise for 2 sets of 10 repetitions.

- You can take just one deep breath in between the sets or more if you need more time to rest.

Tip: This exercise can also be done with weights if you'd like to try some strength-building now or later on when you're ready for it. You can start with one-pound weights and slowly graduate to heavier weights when you become more comfortable and stable.

Chair Torso Circles

This is a simple movement of the torso both in clockwise and counterclockwise directions, coordinated with breath. This hip-opening exercise helps soften and relax the whole of the spine and encourages deep and powerful breathing, which helps rejuvenate your body and calm your mind. The simple hip movements help release the tense energy stored at the lower back and the hips, especially targeting the psoas muscles.

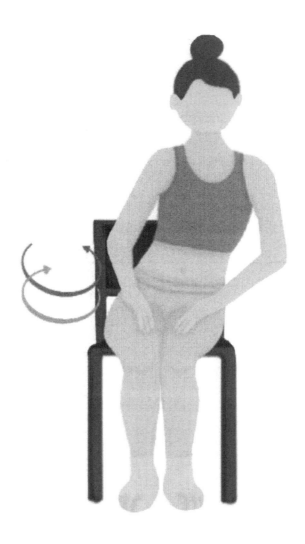

Step-by-Step Instructions:

- Sit on a chair with your back straight and your feet flat on the floor.

- Place your hands on your hips or rest them on your thighs.

- Inhale deeply and as you exhale, engage your core muscles for stability.

- Slowly begin to rotate your torso in a circular motion clockwise.

- Imagine drawing a circle with your upper body.

- Maintain a controlled and fluid movement as you circle your torso.

- Focus on keeping your core muscles engaged, and try to keep your back straight and elongated throughout the exercise.

- Perform the torso circles for 10 circles.

- Then, reverse the direction of the circles, going counterclockwise.

Seated Hand Clenches

I suggest keeping your nails well-trimmed for this exercise so you are not poking your palm when you clench the hand; it's a good motivation to keep on top of your nail trimming!

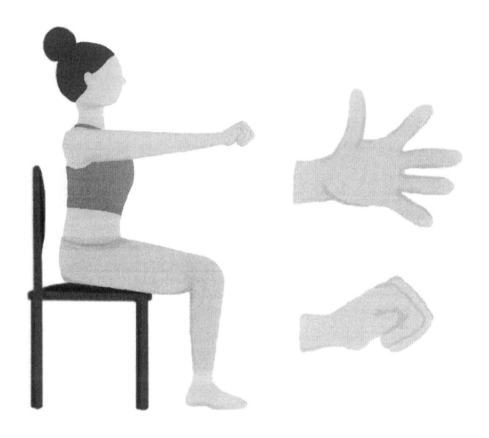

Step-by-Step Instructions:

- Sit on a chair with your back straight and your feet flat on the floor.

- Start with the arms relaxed by the sides.

- Inhale deeply and as you exhale, engage your core muscles for stability.

- Bring your arms out in front of you and pull the shoulder blades back into the socket before starting the hand movement.

- Curl your fingers inward and make a tight fist with both hands.

- Squeeze your hands tightly, engaging the muscles in your hands and forearms.

- Slowly release the tension, opening your hands and extending your fingers.

- Repeat the clenching and releasing of your hands for 2 sets of 10 repetitions.

- You can take just one deep breath in between the sets or more if you need more time to rest.

End with 3–10 Deep Breaths

Ending your routine with deep breaths helps calm you down and cool you down, makes you feel good, and gives your body time to start integrating the results of your exercise.

Step-by-Step Instructions:

- Sit up nice and tall in the chair, toward the edge, so that your back isn't leaning on the backrest of the chair.

- Keep your back straight, spine lengthened, and feet flat and firmly planted on the floor, hip-width apart, with knees bent at a 90-degree angle.

- Place your hands on your thighs, palms facing downward.

- Keep your shoulders in a relaxed and neutral position, your chest raised, and allow your limbs and face to relax.

- Slightly engage your abdominal muscles, pulling your belly button toward your spine and slightly upward.

- Roll your shoulder blades down toward your back, and let your elbows rest at your sides.

- Now close your eyes and inhale deeply through your nose, taking a slow and controlled breath. Once you've taken a full breath in, hold it for a few seconds, but don't strain. Simply hold your breath comfortably.

- Exhale slowly and steadily through your mouth, allowing the air to escape at a controlled pace.

- Inhale deeply again, repeating the process for 3–10 complete breath cycles, depending on how much time you have.

- Slowly and gently open your eyes and release your hands down by your sides to come out of the pose.

These 10-minute seated mobility exercises offer a simple yet effective way to maintain flexibility and improve upper body functionality. Incorporating these exercises into daily routines can help counteract the negative effects of prolonged sitting by promoting better mobility, reducing stiffness, and enhancing overall well-being.

In the next chapter, we will explore a series of chair exercises to improve balance.

10-Minute Seated Mobility Exercises

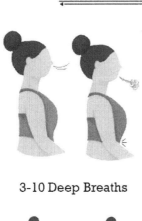

3-10 Deep Breaths

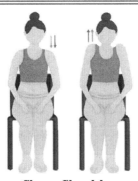

Shrug Shoulders
Up/Down

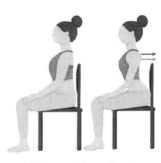

Pull Shoulders Back

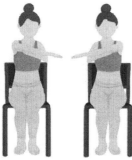

Shoulder Cross -
Arm Stretch

Back of Arm Triceps
Stretch

Chair Calf Stretch Pose

Seated Elbow Circles

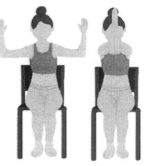

Seated Cactus Arms
Flow

Chair Torso Circles

Seated Hand Clenches

3-10 Deep Breaths

Chapter Four:
Improving Balance: Chair Exercises to Enhance Stability in Just 10 Minutes

Balance is a fundamental aspect of functional fitness, influencing our ability to walk, stand, and perform everyday tasks with ease. With targeted exercises and consistent practice, we can significantly enhance our stability and, therefore, our balance.

In this chapter, we will guide you through a carefully curated set of chair exercises, each one focusing on different aspects of balance and stability. These exercises will engage your core, strengthen your leg muscles, and improve proprioception—your body's awareness of its position in space. Through these simple yet effective chair exercises, we aim to empower seniors with the tools they need to stay steady on their feet and confidently navigate daily activities.

This chapter has some exercises inspired by traditional yoga poses. We will be using the English names and not the Indian names to make them easier to understand. If you're interested in learning more about the traditional Indian names of some yoga poses and more about yoga in general, you can check out my other book, *Quick and Simple Chair Yoga for seniors over 60*!

https://a.co/d/88wdUd9

Now is the time to take control of your balance and embrace the joy of movement!

Start with 3–10 Deep Breaths

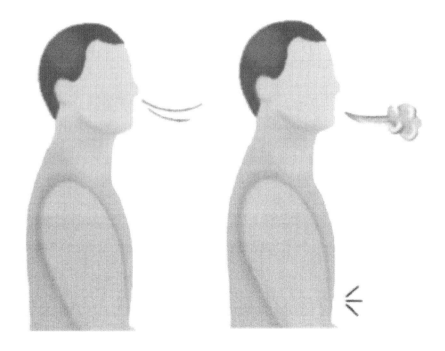

Step-by-Step Instructions:

- Sit up nice and tall in the chair, toward the edge, so that your back isn't leaning on the backrest of the chair.

- Keep your back straight, your spine lengthened, and your feet flat and firmly planted on the floor, hip-width apart, with knees bent at a 90-degree angle.

- Place your hands on your thighs, palms facing downward.

- Keep your shoulders in a relaxed and neutral position, your chest raised, and allow your limbs and face to relax.

- Slightly engage your abdominal muscles, pulling your belly button toward your spine and slightly upward.

- Roll your shoulder blades down toward your back, and let your elbows rest at your sides.

- Now close your eyes and inhale deeply through your nose, taking a slow and controlled breath. Once you've taken a full breath in, hold it for a few seconds, but don't strain. Simply hold your breath comfortably.

- Exhale slowly and steadily through your mouth, allowing the air to escape at a controlled pace.

- Inhale deeply again, repeating the process for 3–10 complete breath cycles, depending on how much time you have.

- Once you've completed the breathing exercise, slowly and gently open your eyes and lower your hands down by your sides to return to the starting position.

Tree Pose with Chair

The tree pose works your hips and legs, stretching and strengthening the muscles in the standing leg while enhancing the mobility and flexibility of the hip joint. This pose also helps improve body awareness and balance.

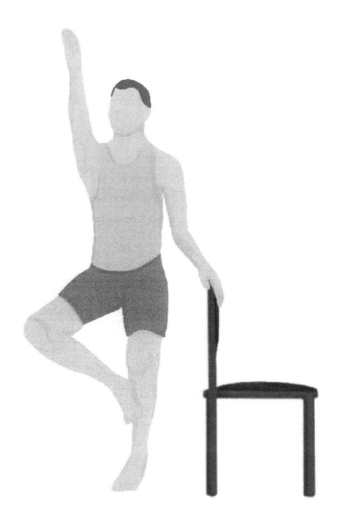

Step-by-Step Instructions:

- Stand alongside a chair, facing away from the chair sideways, with your feet hip-width apart and your back straight.

- Place one hand on the top of the backrest of the chair for support.

- Shift your weight onto the foot that is next to the chair, grounding it firmly into the floor.

- Slowly lift your other foot, the one that is away from the chair, off the ground, bending your knee and bringing the sole of that foot to rest against your inner thigh, calf, or ankle of your standing leg, depending on your ability to balance.

- Avoid placing the foot on the knee joint.

- Find your balance and stability by engaging your core muscles and focusing your gaze on a fixed point in front of you.

- Adjust the position of your foot on the leg to a comfortable height that you can maintain.

- Once you feel stable, let your free arm relax by your side or extend that same arm overhead.

- Hold the tree pose for 30 seconds to 1 minute, or as long as you can maintain your balance and stability.

- Repeat the same steps on the opposite side.

Downward-Facing Dog Pose Variation with Chair

This exercise engages and works your arms, back, hips, and legs, making it beneficial for enhancing balance, increasing flexibility in the back muscles, and strengthening the legs. It proves to be highly advantageous for those aiming to improve their overall physical stability and flexibility.

Step-by-Step Instructions:

- Come to a standing position facing the chair.

- Stand with your feet hip-width apart at a comfortable distance away from the chair.

- Hold onto the chair and walk your feet back, allowing your body to form a 90-degree angle.

- Keep your arms straight and your shoulders relaxed.

- Press your hands firmly into the chair's back and engage your core muscles.

- Lengthen your spine and let your head relax between your arms.

- Shift your weight back toward your hips, feeling a stretch in your hamstrings and calves.

- Keep your heels grounded and your knees slightly bent, if needed, to maintain a comfortable position.

- Take slow, deep breaths, allowing your body to relax and release tension.

- Hold the downward-facing dog pose for 30 seconds to 1 minute, or as long as it feels comfortable for you.

- To release the pose, walk your feet forward toward the chair and slowly come up to a standing position.

- Shake out your legs and take a moment to notice the effects of the pose on your body.

Chair Mountain Pose One Leg Backlift

This pose engages your back muscles, shoulders, abs, and the front of your chest, thus helping to strengthen and stretch these muscles too.

Step-by-Step Instructions:

- Stand facing the chair.

- Stand tall with your feet hip-width apart and your arms relaxed by your sides.

- Inhale deeply and as you exhale, engage your core muscles for stability.

- Hold onto the top or sides of the backrest of the chair for support.

- Find your balance and stability by grounding one foot firmly into the floor.

- Extend your other leg slightly behind you, keeping it in alignment with your body, forming a diagonal line through your body and extended leg.

- Flex your toes and find how far you can go comfortably with balance and alignment.

- Keep your spine elongated, your head neutral, and your gaze looking down. Square the shoulders to be in alignment with each other.

- Hold the mountain pose one leg backlift for 30 seconds to 1 minute, or as long as you can maintain your balance and stability.

- Continue to breathe deeply and maintain good posture throughout the pose.

- To release the pose, slowly lower your foot back to the ground and return to a standing position.

- Repeat the same steps on the opposite side.

Shoulder Pendulum Exercise with Chair

This exercise engages and works the muscles of your shoulders and arms. The shoulder pendulum exercise helps increase your range of motion, improve flexibility, decrease pain, and accelerate your injury recovery process.

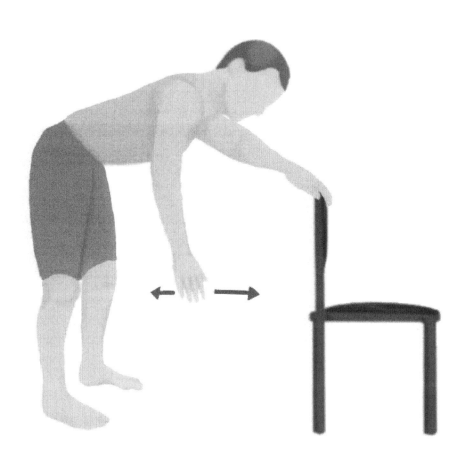

Step-by-Step Instructions:

- Stand facing the chair with your feet hip-width apart. Find your balance and ground yourself through your feet.

- Lean forward slightly, resting your non-working hand on the top of the chair back for support.

- Let your working arm hang down toward the floor, keeping it relaxed.

- Begin by gently swinging your working arm back and forth like a pendulum. Make sure your arm is away from the chair so that you have room to swing your arm safely.

- Start with small and controlled movements, gradually increasing the range of motion.

- Swing your arm forward and backward, allowing it to move freely and without tension.

- As you swing your arm, aim to increase the distance it moves with each swing.

- Focus on relaxing your shoulder and allowing gravity to do the work.

- Perform the shoulder pendulum exercise for 30 seconds to 1 minute.

- After completing the swings, rest for a moment and then switch to the other arm.

- Maintain a relaxed posture throughout the exercise, avoiding any unnecessary tension.

Dancer's Pose with Chair

This pose engages and works your arms, shoulders, back, hips, feet, ankles, core, hamstrings, and chest. It helps stretch and strengthen the mentioned muscles. It also opens up the front of your body—the chest, abdomen, hip flexors, and shoulders—while improving flexibility and stability for your entire body.

Step-by-Step Instructions:

- Stand facing the chair with your feet hip-width apart.

- Find your balance and ground yourself through your feet.

- Hold onto the chair, slowly shift your weight onto one foot, and lift your other foot off the ground.

- Bend one knee and reach back with your same side hand to grasp the outside of your same side foot or ankle.

- If this feels like too much or you feel too unsteady, you can continue to hold the back of the chair with both hands and just bend one leg toward your buttocks and get as close to the buttocks as you can with the heel.

- Inhale and exhale deeply, keep your chest lifted, and your gaze forward.

- Hold the pose for 30 seconds to 1 minute, finding stability and focus.

- Keep your core engaged and your standing leg strong.

- When you're ready to come out of the pose, slowly release your foot and bring it back down to the ground.

- Return to a standing position with both feet on the floor.

- Repeat the pose on the other side.

Half Wide Legged Forward Fold Pose with Chair

This exercise is good for stretching and strengthening your hamstrings, calves, hips, feet, ankles, and legs, as well as building awareness of protecting your lower back. Also, it calms and relaxes your mind, alleviating feelings and thoughts of anxiety.

Step-by-Step Instructions:

- Stand facing the chair with your feet hip-width apart.

- The chair backrest can be facing you, or the chair seat can be facing you. Depending on your flexibility, you'll need to try this pose once to decide how to set up the chair going forward.

- Place your hands on your hips and take a moment to lengthen your spine, ensuring that your chest is lifted and your shoulders are relaxed.

- Inhale deeply and, as you exhale, hold the chair, and simultaneously walk back as you begin to hinge forward from your hips, maintaining a long spine until you are at a 90-degree angle.

- Then, step your feet out until they are in a wide-legged stance that is manageable for you. You should feel a gentle stretch in the back of your legs, particularly in your hamstrings and inner thighs, but not pain.

- Adjust your hands, placing them on the seat or the backrest for support, depending on your flexibility.

- Keep your spine long and your chest open. Relax your neck and allow your head to relax, gazing toward the floor.

- Continue to breathe deeply and hold the pose for 30 seconds to 1 minute, allowing yourself to surrender to the stretch.

- Feel free to adjust the chair's position or the width of your stance to find a comfortable stretch.

- To come out of the pose, engage your core muscles and slowly rise back up, maintaining the length of your spine.

End with 3–10 Deep Breaths

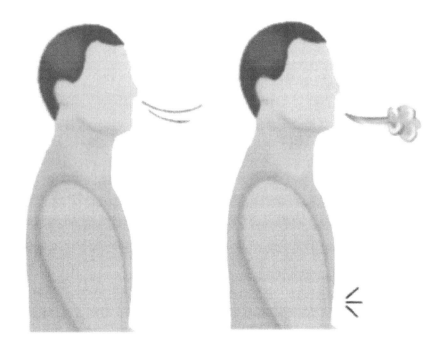

Step-by-Step Instructions:

- Sit up nice and tall in the chair, toward the edge, so that your back isn't leaning on the backrest of the chair.

- Keep your back straight, spine lengthened, and feet flat and firmly planted on the floor, hip-width apart, with knees bent at a 90-degree angle.

- Place your hands on your thighs, palms facing downward.

- Keep your shoulders in a relaxed and neutral position, your chest raised, and allow your limbs and face to relax.

- Slightly engage your abdominal muscles, pulling your belly button toward your spine and slightly upward.

- Roll your shoulder blades down toward your back, and let your elbows rest at your sides.

- Now close your eyes and inhale deeply through your nose, taking a slow and controlled breath. Once you've taken a full breath in, hold it for a few seconds, but don't strain. Simply hold your breath comfortably.

- Exhale slowly and steadily through your mouth, allowing the air to escape at a controlled pace.

- Inhale deeply again, repeating the process for 3–10 complete breath cycles, depending on how much time you have.

- Slowly and gently open your eyes and release your hands down by your sides to come out of the pose.

Chair Exercises to Enhance Stability in Just 10 Minutes

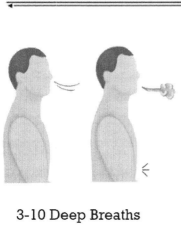  

3-10 Deep Breaths   Tree Pose With Chair   Downward Facing Dog
                                                         Pose Variation
                                                         With Chair

Chair Mountain Pose   Shoulder Pendulum
One Leg Backlift   Exercise with Chair   Dancer's Pose With Chair

 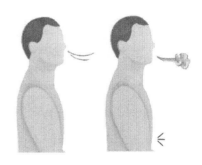

Half Wide Legged Forward   3-10 Deep Breaths
Fold Pose with Chair

Chapter Five:
10-Minute Strengthening and Toning:
Chair Exercises for Lower Body Strength

As we all know, our lower half serves as the foundation of support for our entire body, playing a vital role in our ability to walk and move. Our lower body contains most of the largest muscles in our body, making its strengthening not only crucial in our quest for a healthy physique but also in maintaining overall health.

The benefits of strengthening your lower body are multifaceted and far-reaching. Not only does it contribute to greater stability and balance, but it also enhances overall functional fitness. Whether it's getting up from a chair, climbing stairs, or walking around the house, a stronger lower body is the key to performing these activities with ease and grace.

Throughout this chapter, you will be guided through a series of gentle yet effective exercises carefully curated to target various muscle groups in your lower body. From your thighs and hips to your calves and ankles, each exercise aims to improve flexibility, enhance circulation, and build muscular strength. Through these simple yet effective chair exercises, we aim to empower seniors with the tools they need to stay active, healthy, and confident in their daily lives.

Remember, consistency is key. By dedicating just 10 minutes of your day to these chair exercises, you can make significant strides toward improving your lower body strength and overall well-being. So, let's get started on this journey toward a healthier, stronger you!

Start with 3–10 Deep Breaths

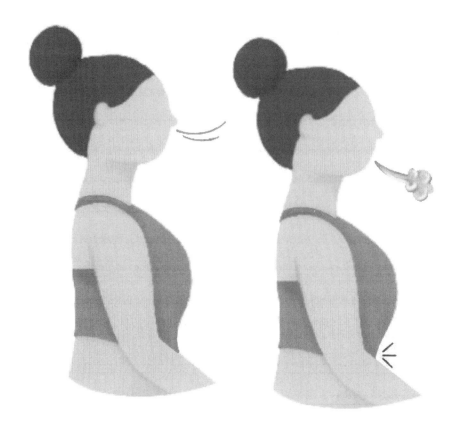

Step-by-Step Instructions:

- Sit up nice and tall in the chair, toward the edge, so that your back isn't leaning on the backrest of the chair.

- Keep your back straight, spine lengthened, and feet flat and firmly planted on the floor, hip-width apart, with knees bent at a 90-degree angle.

- Place your hands on your thighs, palms facing downward.

- Keep your shoulders in a relaxed and neutral position, your chest raised, and allow your limbs and face to relax.

- Slightly engage your abdominal muscles, pulling your belly button toward your spine and slightly upward.

- Roll your shoulder blades down toward your back, and let your elbows rest at your sides.

- Now close your eyes and inhale deeply through your nose, taking a slow and controlled breath. Once you've taken a full breath in, hold it for a few seconds, but don't strain. Simply hold your breath comfortably.

- Exhale slowly and steadily through your mouth, allowing the air to escape at a controlled pace.

- Inhale deeply again, repeating the process for 3–10 complete breath cycles, depending on how much time you have.

- Once you've completed the breathing exercise, slowly and gently open your eyes and lower your hands down by your sides to return to the starting position.

Heel Raises with Chair

This exercise engages your calf muscles and inner thighs. Performing heel raises effectively strengthens the opposite sides of your feet and the muscles in your lower legs, contributing to increased stability, mobility, and flexibility of the ankle joint.

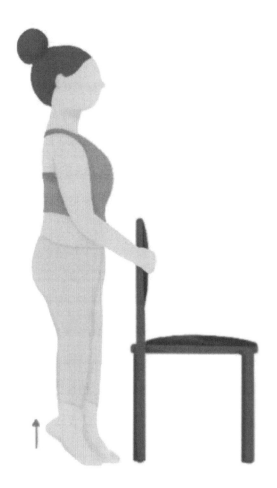

Step-by-Step Instructions:

- Stand behind a chair, placing your hands lightly on the sides or top of the backrest for support.

- Position your feet hip-width apart, ensuring that your weight is evenly distributed.

- Engage your core muscles to maintain stability and good posture throughout the exercise.

- Slowly rise onto your tiptoes, lifting your heels off the ground.

- Gradually lower your heels back down to the starting position.

- Perform the heel raises for 2 sets of 15 repetitions.

- Keep your ankles straight and aligned with your legs as you do these.

Hip Abduction with Chair

This exercise engages your hips and legs. It helps strengthen the muscles in your outer thighs and hip bones, contributing to improved balance and walking abilities and providing overall stability and support for the body.

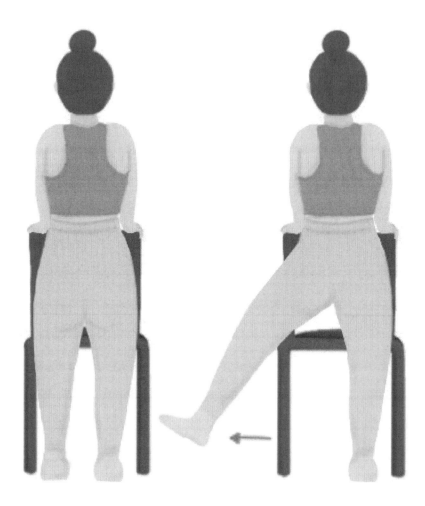

Step-by-Step Instructions:

- Stand behind the chair and hold onto it for support.

- Stand tall with your feet hip-width apart and your core engaged.

- Shift your weight onto one leg and slightly bend your knee.

- Lift your other leg out to the side, keeping it straight and maintaining control.

- Slowly lower your leg back down to the starting position.

- Perform the hip abduction exercise for 15 repetitions.

- Aim to lift your leg as high as you comfortably can as you do these without compromising your balance or form.

- Keep your toes pointing forward and your hips facing forward throughout the movement.

- Repeat the pose on the other side.

Hip Extension Leg Lift with Chair

This exercise engages your glutes and hamstrings. It effectively strengthens the glutes, hamstrings, quads, and core, maintaining a neutral spine and enhancing balance and stability.

Step-by-Step Instructions:

- Stand behind a chair, placing your hands lightly on the sides or top of the backrest for support.

- Position your feet hip-width apart, ensuring that your weight is evenly distributed.

- Engage your core muscles to maintain stability and good posture throughout the exercise.

- Slowly lift one leg straight back, extending it behind you.

- Gradually lower your leg back down to the starting position.

- Perform the hip extension exercise for 15 repetitions on one leg.

- Keep your leg straight and your toes pointing forward as you do these.

- Aim to lift your leg as high as you comfortably can throughout the movement without compromising your balance or form.

- Maintain a slight bend in your supporting leg for stability as you do these.

- Repeat the pose on the other side.

Flamingo Swing with Chair

This movement engages your core and leg muscles. It helps strengthen your core and legs, leading to improved balance and stability.

Step-by-Step Instructions:

- Stand alongside a chair, facing away from the chair sideways, placing one hand lightly on the backrest for support.

- Position your feet hip-width apart, ensuring that your weight is evenly distributed.

- Engage your core muscles to maintain stability and good posture throughout the exercise.

- Shift your weight onto the inner foot, the one next to the chair.

- Swing the other leg, the outer leg that is away from the chair, forward and back with control.

- Perform the flamingo swing for 30 seconds to 1 minute.

- Repeat the pose on the other side.

Hamstring Curl with Chair

This exercise engages your hamstrings, quads, and knees. It helps strengthen these muscles, thus enhancing mobility and balance.

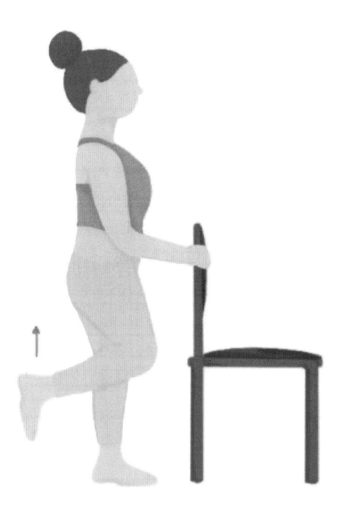

Step-by-Step Instructions:

- Stand tall with your feet hip-width apart and your hands resting lightly on the sides or top of the backrest of the chair for support.

- Engage your core muscles to maintain stability and good posture throughout the exercise.

- Shift your weight onto one foot.

- Bend your other knee and lift that foot off the ground, bringing your heel toward your glutes.

- Slowly lower your right foot back to the starting position.

- Perform the hamstring curl exercise for 15 repetitions on one leg.

- Aim to bring your foot as close to your glutes as possible as you do these, feeling the contraction in your hamstring muscles.

- Keep your upper body stable, and avoid leaning forward or backward throughout the movement.

- Repeat the pose on the other side.

End with 3–10 Deep Breaths

Step-by-Step Instructions:

- Sit up nice and tall in the chair, toward the edge, so that your back isn't leaning on the backrest of the chair.

- Keep your back straight, your spine lengthened, and your feet flat and firmly planted on the floor, hip-width apart, with knees bent at a 90-degree angle.

- Place your hands on your thighs, palms facing downward.

- Keep your shoulders in a relaxed and neutral position, your chest raised, and allow your limbs and face to relax.

- Slightly engage your abdominal muscles, pulling your belly button toward your spine and slightly upward.

- Roll your shoulder blades down toward your back, and let your elbows rest at your sides.

- Now close your eyes and inhale deeply through your nose, taking a slow and controlled breath. Once you've taken a full breath in, hold it for a few seconds, but don't strain. Simply hold your breath comfortably.

- Exhale slowly and steadily through your mouth, allowing the air to escape at a controlled pace.

- Inhale deeply again, repeating the process for 3–10 complete breath cycles, depending on how much time you have.

- Slowly and gently open your eyes and release your hands down by your sides to come out of the pose.

10-Minute Strengthening and Toning Exercises

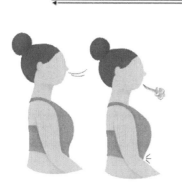

3-10 Deep Breaths

Heel Raises With Chair

Hip Abduction
With Chair

Hip Extension Leg Lift
With Chair

Flamingo Swing
With Chair

Hamstring Curl
With Chair

3-10 Deep Breaths

Your Chance to Be an Inspiration!

"The longer I live, the more beautiful life becomes." – Frank Lloyd Wright

As you may remember from the introduction, I shared that my mom has stayed healthy by exercising regularly and is very fit and spry at 81 years old!

I do these chair exercises with her regularly and we both agree that they keep her limber and moving well for all of her life activities. I love telling her story to everyone I know to inspire others!

As you grow in strength and energy, I've no doubt that you'll feel the same impulse… and the best part is, you can start spreading the word right now.

I'd like to invite you to take a moment to inspire other readers to become the masters of their own health and jump into those golden years full of strength and vitality.

By leaving a review of this book on Amazon, you'll inspire new readers to build their strength and unlock energy they'd forgotten they even had.

The simple act of sharing your experience of this book and a little about its contents will light the path to a strong and vibrant future for many more people.

Thank you so much for your support. I'm so excited about the impact we can have simply by talking about this.

https://www.amazon.com/review/create-review/?asin=B0CM6XYT4L

Chapter Six:
Mindful Eating: A Key to Healthy Aging

In the quest for longevity and well-being, the role of diet in promoting healthy aging cannot be overstated. Over the years, numerous dietary approaches have emerged, each claiming to hold the key to a longer and more vibrant life. Among these, the Paleo diet stands out as a promising contender, rooted in the principles of eating well to age better. In this chapter, we delve into the powerful synergy between phytonutrients and the Paleo diet, uncovering the science behind their impact on healthy aging.

Phytonutrients are bioactive compounds found in plants that possess various health benefits, including anti-inflammatory effects and immune system support.

The Paleo diet, inspired by our ancestors' dietary habits during the Paleolithic era, emphasizes whole, unprocessed foods rich in nutrients and devoid of modern additives. This dietary approach centers around consuming lean proteins, abundant fruits and vegetables, nuts, seeds, and healthy fats. By adopting a Paleo lifestyle, individuals naturally increase their intake of phytonutrients, setting the stage for healthy aging.

- **Abundance of Colorful Plant Foods:** A cornerstone of the Paleo diet is the inclusion of colorful, non-starchy vegetables and fruits. These vibrant foods are teeming with phytonutrients. These potent compounds help combat oxidative stress, reduce inflammation, and bolster the immune system, promoting resilience as we age.

- **Lean Proteins:** The Paleo diet encourages the consumption of high-quality, lean proteins from sources like grass-fed meats, fish, and free-range poultry. These proteins provide essential amino acids, zinc, and selenium, all of which play critical roles in supporting the body's phytonutrient defense mechanisms.

- **Healthy Fats:** Embracing healthy fats like those found in avocados, nuts, and olive oil helps maintain cardiovascular health and cognitive function.

Phytonutrients and Their Benefits

The term "phyto" means plant. Phytonutrients are advantageous nutrients present in plant-based foods, including vegetables, fruits, nuts, and seeds. Teas, herbs, and spices also contain a plethora of diverse phytonutrients.

These compounds offer various benefits to our health. Some phytonutrients shield our cells from damage, while others support the body's natural detoxification processes. Some even exhibit anti-inflammatory properties and contribute to the well-being of our brain, heart, skin, eyes, and liver.

Their Benefits:

- *Enhance Immune Function*

Phytonutrients have been shown to have immunomodulatory properties, meaning they can positively influence the immune system. For instance, flavonoids found in fruits and vegetables have been associated with an enhanced immune response and reduced inflammation.

A study published in "Molecules" (Liu et al., 2021) indicated that the consumption of anthocyanins, a type of flavonoid, was linked to improved immune function and reduced inflammation in older adults. A stronger immune system helps protect the body and promotes overall wellness as we age.

- *Support Cardiovascular Health and Help Maintain Healthy Blood Pressure Levels*

Phytonutrients offer promising benefits for maintaining a healthy heart and blood pressure levels. For instance, resveratrol, found in grapes and berries, has been studied extensively for its potential cardiovascular benefits.

Research suggests that resveratrol can improve heart health by enhancing blood flow (Dyck et al., 2019). Moreover, a randomized controlled trial published in "Nutrients" (Rees et al., 2018) found that increased intake of dietary flavonoids was associated with reduced blood pressure levels in older individuals, supporting cardiovascular function.

- *Promote Healthy Digestion and Gut Microbiome Balance*

Phytonutrients, especially fiber-rich compounds, play a vital role in maintaining a healthy gut microbiome and improving digestive function.

A study published in Frontiers in Nutrition highlighted that the consumption of phytonutrient-rich foods improved gut microbial diversity and promoted beneficial bacteria, leading to better digestive health in elderly participants (Kan et al., 2022).

- *Aid in Detoxification and Liver Function for Optimal Body Cleansing*

Phytonutrients aid in the elimination of harmful substances and support optimal liver function. For example, sulforaphane, found in cruciferous vegetables, has been shown to enhance detoxification pathways in the liver.

A study published in "Nutrients" (Monjotin et al., 2022) demonstrated that specific phytonutrients facilitated detoxification, contributed to body cleansing, and improved overall well-being.

- *Enhance Brain Health and Cognitive Function for Sharper Mental Acuity*

Flavonoids and other phytochemicals have shown neuroprotective properties, helping to preserve brain health and enhance cognitive function.

A 2020 systematic review published in Aging Research Reviews revealed that regular intake of flavonoids was associated with improved mental acuity in older adults (Godos et al., 2020). By supporting brain health, phytonutrients can help us maintain mental sharpness and cognitive abilities as we age.

- *Support Healthy Aging*

Phytonutrients contribute to overall healthy aging by enhancing overall well-being. A longitudinal study published in The Journals of Nutritional Biochemistry (Si & Liu, 2014) found that individuals with higher dietary intakes of phytonutrients showed healthier aging trajectories. By supporting various bodily functions and promoting overall health, phytonutrients can help us age gracefully and maintain an active lifestyle.

- *Boost Skin Health and Radiance by Promoting a Youthful Complexion*

Phytonutrients can aid in maintaining a healthy complexion by protecting the skin from UV-induced damage and supporting collagen production. A clinical trial published in the Journal of Nutrients (Evans & Johnson, 2010) revealed that phytonutrient supplementation improved skin elasticity, promoting skin health and radiance.

- *Aid in Weight Management by Supporting Metabolism and Satiety*

Phytonutrients can aid in weight management by supporting metabolism and promoting satiety. For example, green tea catechins, a type of phytonutrient, have been shown to increase fat oxidation and lead to a reduction in body weight in older adults. Several studies (Basu et al., 2023; Meydani & Hasan, 2010) have reported these findings, indicating that phytonutrients may be beneficial for weight management in aging populations.

- *Promote Cellular Repair*

Phytonutrients, particularly those with anti-inflammatory properties, support cellular repair mechanisms. A 2022 study published in "Nutrients" showed that certain phytonutrients helped protect and repair cellular structures, contributing to better cellular health and overall well-being (Monjotin et al., 2022).

- *Aid in Supporting Respiratory Health*

Phytonutrients with anti-inflammatory and immunomodulatory properties can aid in supporting respiratory health. A clinical trial published in "Nutrients" (Monjotin et al., 2022) demonstrated that a phytonutrient-rich diet improved lung function in elderly participants.

Phytonutrients: Eat the Rainbow!

The color of plant foods is influenced by the presence of phytonutrients. By incorporating foods from all color groups into our diet, we can enjoy a wide range of these beneficial compounds. Generally, the darker the color of the food, the higher its phytonutrient content. To reap the benefits, it is recommended to aim for at least one serving from each color group every day.

Here's a list of fruits and vegetables categorized by their colors, along with the corresponding phytonutrients they possess and the specific foods where you can find them.

Red Phytonutrients: Apples, Raspberries, and Beets: Red fruits and vegetables owe their color to phytonutrients such as lycopene and anthocyanins. Apples, raspberries, and beets contain anthocyanins, which have phytonutrient and anti-inflammatory properties. Several studies have shown that anthocyanins may contribute to better cardiovascular health and cognitive function in aging individuals (Hair et al., 2021; Wallace, 2011). Consuming a variety of red foods can thus help support heart health and brain function.

Orange and Yellow Phytonutrients: Pumpkin, Carrots, and Papaya: Orange and yellow fruits and vegetables are rich in carotenoids, such as beta-carotene, which the body can convert into vitamin A. Vitamin A is essential for maintaining healthy vision, skin, and immune function. Additionally, beta-carotene and other carotenoids act as phytonutrients, protecting the body from oxidative stress. Including pumpkin, carrots, papaya, and other yellow and orange foods in our diet can help preserve eye health and boost immunity as we age (Chapman et al., 2018).

Green Phytonutrients: Avocado, Broccoli, and Cantaloupe: Green vegetables contain a range of phytonutrients such as lutein, zeaxanthin, and sulforaphane. Lutein and zeaxanthin are carotenoids that accumulate in the eyes, specifically the macula, where they act as natural sunscreens and protect against harmful UV rays. Sulforaphane, found in broccoli, has gained attention for its potential to enhance the body's natural defense mechanisms and promote detoxification (Houghton, 2019). Green foods like avocado, broccoli, and cantaloupe are excellent choices to support eye health and boost the body's phytonutrient capacity.

Purple Phytonutrients: Eggplant, Grapes, Blueberries, and Blackberries: The deep purple hue in fruits and vegetables comes from anthocyanins, which we discussed earlier in the red foods category. Apart from the benefits to heart and brain health, purple phytonutrients have also shown promise in supporting gut health. Research suggests that these compounds can positively influence the gut microbiota, promoting a balanced and diverse microbial community in the digestive system (Kan et al., 2022). A healthy gut microbiome is associated with better digestion, reduced inflammation, and improved immune function. Including eggplant, grapes, blueberries, and blackberries in the diet can contribute to a healthier gut as we age.

White Phytonutrients: Onions, Mushrooms, and Pears: White foods may not be as visually striking as the other colors, but they still contain valuable phytonutrients. Onions, for instance, contain quercetin, a flavonoid known for its anti-inflammatory properties. Mushrooms are an excellent source of ergothioneine, a unique phytonutrient that plays a role in protecting cells from oxidative damage (Fu & Shen, 2022). Pears are rich in dietary fiber, which aids in digestion and supports a healthy gut. Incorporating white foods like onions, mushrooms, and pears into the diet can help promote better digestion as we age.

Eating Well, Aging Better: Introduction to the Paleo Diet

As the pursuit of healthier lifestyles gains momentum, the Paleo diet has emerged as a popular choice among health-conscious individuals seeking to enhance their well-being and vitality. The Paleo diet, also known as the "caveman diet" or "Paleolithic diet," draws its inspiration from the dietary habits of our ancient ancestors. The fundamental premise of this diet is to return to a more primal and natural way of eating, which emphasizes whole, unprocessed foods that our ancestors would have consumed.

Out of all the diets that have become trendy over the years, I have chosen to present the Paleo diet to you as an option because it has helped my mom and me become so much healthier, and many symptoms have fallen away for both of us by adhering to this diet. I have tried many diets over the years, trying to find optimal health and energy, and this one has been the best one for myself and my mom! If you're curious, it's worth giving it a shot!

The Paleo diet centers on a few core principles that form the foundation of its approach to nutrition. Firstly, the diet emphasizes the consumption of whole, unprocessed foods, avoiding the myriad of artificial additives and preservatives that have become commonplace in modern diets. By focusing on foods in their natural state, the diet seeks to promote better digestion and overall health.

At the heart of the Paleo diet is a focus on lean meats, fish, fruits, vegetables, nuts, and seeds. These food groups provide essential nutrients, such as protein, healthy fats, vitamins, and minerals, which are vital for maintaining optimal health. Lean meats and fish supply ample protein, which is essential for muscle maintenance, tissue repair, and overall body function. Meanwhile, fruits and vegetables offer a rich source of vitamins, minerals, and phytonutrients, supporting the immune system.

In contrast to many contemporary diets, the Paleo diet excludes processed foods, grains, dairy, legumes, and added sugars. The exclusion of these food groups is based on the belief that they might be responsible for various health issues. By avoiding these foods, the Paleo diet aims to improve overall well-being.

One of the key philosophies of the Paleo diet is its attempt to mimic the dietary patterns of early human hunter-gatherers. Advocates argue that our bodies are genetically adapted to thrive on the foods that our ancestors ate during the Paleolithic era, which predated the advent of agriculture and animal domestication. In this sense, the diet aligns with the notion that our bodies are better suited to handle the foods available in the pre-agricultural era.

The emphasis on consuming foods in their most natural, unaltered form is another central principle of the Paleo diet. This approach promotes nutrient-dense foods, as processing can deplete the nutritional content of various edibles. By opting for foods in their whole state, followers of the Paleo diet seek to maximize their intake of essential nutrients, contributing to improved overall health.

A distinctive aspect of the Paleo diet is its encouragement of a higher intake of healthy fats from sources like avocados and nuts. Unlike the low-fat diet fads of the past, the Paleo diet recognizes that healthy fats are essential for various bodily functions, including hormone production, brain health, and the absorption of fat-soluble vitamins. By incorporating these healthy fats into their meals, adherents aim to optimize their health and well-being.

Furthermore, the Paleo diet prioritizes quality sourcing, advocating for organic and grass-fed options whenever possible. This commitment to sustainable agriculture aligns with the broader movement toward environmentally conscious food choices. By choosing foods that are raised and produced ethically and sustainably, Paleo enthusiasts not only support their health but also contribute positively to the planet.

One of the reasons the Paleo diet has gained popularity is its support of a low-carb, high-protein approach to eating. By reducing carbohydrate intake and increasing protein consumption, the diet aims to stabilize blood sugar levels and promote fat loss. For those looking to manage their weight or improve their body composition, this aspect of the Paleo diet can be particularly appealing.

Beyond its nutritional guidelines, the Paleo diet is also a lifestyle approach that encompasses overall wellness. In addition to eating well, adherents are encouraged to engage in regular physical activity, prioritize sleep, manage stress, and foster meaningful connections with others. This holistic perspective acknowledges that optimal health involves more than just dietary choices; it involves a balanced and mindful way of living.

Benefits of the Paleo Diet

- *Promotes Weight Loss through Whole, Nutrient-Dense Foods*

The Paleo diet offers a promising solution to weight loss by prioritizing whole, nutrient-dense foods that are naturally low in calories and high in essential nutrients. By eliminating processed and refined foods that are often laden with empty calories, the diet helps control caloric intake without compromising nutritional needs.

The high fiber content of fruits and vegetables in the Paleo diet also contributes to satiety, helping individuals feel fuller longer and reducing overall food consumption. Studies have shown that the Paleo diet can lead to sustainable weight loss and improvements in body composition, making it an attractive option for those seeking to achieve and maintain a healthy weight (Turner-McGrievy et al., 2017).

- *Supports Stable Blood Sugar Levels and Improved Insulin Sensitivity*

The Paleo diet's exclusion of refined carbohydrates and added sugars, which are known to cause rapid spikes in blood glucose levels, helps maintain stable blood sugar levels throughout the day. Research has demonstrated that the Paleo diet can lead to improvements in insulin sensitivity (Mohammadi et al., 2019). Moreover, a stable blood sugar level contributes to sustained energy levels and prevents energy crashes, leading to improved overall well-being.

- *Enhances Energy Levels with Consistent and Steady Fuel*

Energy is a vital aspect of daily life, impacting productivity, physical performance, and overall mood. The Paleo diet provides a consistent and steady source of energy by emphasizing nutrient-dense foods that are rich in complex carbohydrates, healthy fats, and proteins. Unlike the temporary energy spikes from sugary or processed foods, the Paleo diet's balanced macronutrient composition sustains energy levels throughout the day.

Moreover, the inclusion of healthy fats, such as those from avocados, nuts, and olive oil, provides a long-lasting and stable source of energy. Studies have shown that individuals following the Paleo diet experience improved energy expenditure and exercise performance, further highlighting its positive impact on energy levels and physical activity (Manheimer et al., 2015).

- *Improves Gut Health with a Balanced Microbiome*

The health of the gut microbiome has emerged as a crucial factor in overall well-being. The Paleo diet's exclusion of processed foods, artificial additives, and refined sugars helps maintain a balanced and diverse microbiome, contributing to better digestive health and immune function.

Furthermore, the Paleo diet's emphasis on fibrous fruits and vegetables provides prebiotic compounds that support the growth of beneficial gut bacteria. Studies have indicated that a diet rich in prebiotic foods positively influences gut microbiota composition, promoting a healthier digestive environment (Barone et al., 2019).

- *Provides a High Intake of Vitamins, Minerals, and Phytonutrients*

Vitamins, minerals, and phytonutrients play vital roles in maintaining various bodily functions, supporting immune health, and protecting against oxidative stress. The Paleo diet's focus on natural, whole foods ensures a high intake of these essential nutrients.

Fruits and vegetables are rich sources of vitamins, including vitamin C, vitamin A, and various B vitamins. They also provide a plethora of minerals, such as potassium, magnesium, and calcium. Phytonutrient-rich foods in the Paleo diet, such as berries, dark leafy greens, and nuts, are especially full of these beneficial components.

- *Encourages Consumption of Lean Proteins: Supporting Muscle Growth and Repair*

A cornerstone of the Paleo diet is the inclusion of lean proteins derived from sources such as fish, poultry, and nuts. These high-quality proteins play a crucial role in supporting muscle growth, repair, and overall tissue maintenance. Protein is composed of amino acids, which are the building blocks of muscles, enzymes, and various other essential molecules in the body.

Studies have shown that a higher protein intake is associated with improved muscle mass, strength, and function, especially in combination with regular physical activity (Carbone & Pasiakos, 2019). By prioritizing lean proteins, the Paleo diet ensures that individuals have the necessary nutrients to maintain muscle mass and optimize physical performance.

- *Improves Cognitive Function: Supporting Brain Health*

The Paleo diet has garnered attention for its potential to enhance cognitive function and support brain health. Key components of the diet, such as omega-3 fatty acids from sources like fish and nuts, have been linked to brain development and cognitive performance. Omega-3 fatty acids play an essential role in maintaining the structural integrity of brain cells and facilitating communication between neurons.

- *Supports a Natural, Unprocessed Food Approach: Aligning with Our Evolutionary Heritage*

One of the fundamental principles of the Paleo diet is its alignment with our evolutionary heritage. Proponents of the diet argue that our bodies are genetically adapted to thrive on the foods that our ancestors consumed during the Paleolithic era. During this time, humans primarily relied on natural, unprocessed foods such as meat, fish, fruits, vegetables, nuts, and seeds for sustenance.

By adopting a natural, unprocessed food approach, the Paleo diet promotes nutrient-dense choices. This alignment with our evolutionary history has led to the belief that the Paleo diet might be better suited to meet the nutritional needs of the human body.

- *Promotes a Balanced Macronutrient Ratio: Reducing Reliance on Refined Carbohydrates*

The Paleo diet encourages a balanced macronutrient ratio, incorporating healthy fats, proteins, and unrefined carbohydrates from whole, nutrient-rich sources.

Healthy fats, such as those found in avocados, nuts, and olive oil, are essential for brain health, hormone regulation, and the absorption of fat-soluble vitamins. Proteins provide a steady source of energy and support muscle growth and repair, as discussed earlier. Carbohydrates from fruits and vegetables provide essential vitamins, minerals, and fiber without causing significant blood sugar spikes.

- *Encourages Mindful Eating: Focusing on Whole, Unprocessed Ingredients*

Mindful eating is an essential aspect of the Paleo diet, encouraging individuals to pay closer attention to their food choices and eating behaviors. By prioritizing whole, unprocessed ingredients, individuals become more aware of the nutritional content and sourcing of their meals. Mindful eating also involves savoring the flavors, textures, and aromas of foods, which can lead to a greater sense of satisfaction and enjoyment during mealtimes.

Practicing mindful eating can also help prevent overeating and improve digestion as individuals become more attuned to their bodies' hunger and fullness cues. By avoiding processed and convenience foods, individuals following the Paleo diet can foster a deeper connection to the food they consume and develop a more conscious and balanced relationship with eating.

The following is a meal plan for 5 to 6 days' worth of lunches and dinners. This is the type of thing that could be cooked on a Sunday and then eaten throughout the week—Monday through Friday.

It is based on one person living alone. If you're cooking for two people, this could last you 3 to 4 days, or you could double the recipes to last you 5 to 6 days for two people.

It's a lot of meals, so you can have it to last you through the week. It can be very helpful when changing eating habits to just have healthy food ready to go in your fridge when you're hungry!

However, if it's not your style to cook so much food at once, you could always half the amount of the recipes and just eat them over a few days. It's totally up to you!

It's good to use Pyrex or stainless steel containers with lids to portion them out after you cook so that you have the meals ready to grab and go when you're heading out the door, or you can heat them right in the container if you're eating at home.

I did not include breakfast items, as I find breakfast can be done very simply. You could make extra poached eggs and extra sweet potatoes and have a very simple breakfast meal of eggs and sweet potatoes. Or if you like it even lighter than that, just apple slices with almond butter are a nice option.

The Quick and Simple Power Paleo Meal Plan

Meal Prep Recipe List

1. Baked Herbed Ground Meat (Turkey or Chicken)

2. Marinated Chicken Thighs with Italian Herbs

3. Quick Baked Salmon (and Salmon Caper Salad)

4. Simple Poached Eggs

5. Cubed Sweet Potatoes

6. Curried Vegetable Sauté

7. Perfectly Soft Broccoli

8. Minced Cilantro

Baked Herbed Ground Meat (Turkey or Chicken)

☐ 1 pound container of ground meat

☐ 1 teaspoon salt

☐ 1 teaspoon Italian herbs

1. Line a large, shallow baking pan with parchment paper.
2. Open up one 1-pound container of ground meat and empty it onto the parchment paper.
3. Press the meat into parchment paper with a spatula and break it up so it's easier to bake.
4. Always wash your hands after handling raw meat.
5. Place in 375° oven for 30 minutes, and then check the temperature.
6. It must be at least 160° in internal temperature.
7. You may need to put it back for another 15 to 20 minutes.
8. Remove from the oven and allow to cool.
9. Chop meat very small, add 1 teaspoon salt, and stir well to incorporate salt.
10. Place in a container to store in the fridge until meal assembly.

Marinated Chicken Thighs with Italian Herbs

- ☐ 2 pounds of boneless, skinless chicken thighs
- ☐ 1/3 cup filtered water
- ☐ 1/3 cup apple cider vinegar
- ☐ 1 teaspoon salt
- ☐ 1 teaspoon Italian herbs

1. Preheat the oven to 375°.
2. Mix water, vinegar, herbs, and salt in a large stainless steel bowl.
3. Add chicken to bowl and coat in marinade.
4. Cover it up and marinate the chicken for 30–60 minutes in the refrigerator.
5. Put it on a stainless steel baking sheet and spread the thighs out.
6. Bake chicken in the preheated oven, starting with 25 minutes.
7. The internal temperature should read 165° when cooked completely.
8. If not done, put it back for 5-minute increments until it reaches 165°.

Quick Baked Salmon (and Salmon Caper Salad)

- ☐ 2 packages of thawed salmon
- ☐ 1/4 cup of water
- ☐ 1/2 teaspoon salt
- ☐ 1 teaspoon Italian herbs

Salmon Caper Salad

- ☐ One Recipe – Quick Baked Salmon
- ☐ 1 tablespoon capers
- ☐ 1/3 cup mayonnaise made with olive oil or avocado oil

1. Preheat the oven to 425°.
2. Cut open the thawed salmon packages (6 ounces per package) and keep juices; empty juices directly onto the baking pan.
3. Then sprinkle 1/4 cup of water over the salmon.
4. Then sprinkle 1/2 of a teaspoon salt and 1 teaspoon herb mix over the salmon.
5. Bake for 9 minutes or until a meat thermometer says it's reached 130° internal temperature.

Salmon Caper Salad

After it's cooled, chop it up with the metal spatula, then mix in with:

- ☐ 1/3 cup mayonnaise made with olive oil or avocado oil
- ☐ 1 tablespoon capers
- ☐ 1 teaspoon Italian herbs

Simple Poached Eggs

- ☐ 8 eggs
- ☐ 2 tablespoons apple cider vinegar
- ☐ 2 tablespoons salt + 1/2 teaspoon salt

1. Boil water with a cover on high.
2. Add 2 tablespoons salt.
3. Break 8 eggs into a pot of boiling water.
4. Add 2 tablespoons apple cider vinegar.
5. Set a timer for 4 minutes.
6. Leave uncovered, and when it starts boiling again, turn it down to medium.
7. Walk away from the eggs and let them do their thing.
8. After 4 minutes, scoop out the eggs with a stainless steel-slotted spoon into a container.
9. They will look wild and crazy at first in the water, but when you come back, they will have formed into little poached eggs!
10. Put in the fridge until meal assembly time.
11. Sprinkle 1/2 of a teaspoon salt over the eggs.

Cubed Sweet Potatoes

- □ 16 cups chopped sweet potatoes—scrubbed and peeled
- □ 1 tablespoon salt
- □ 2 tablespoons coconut oil or avocado oil

1. Fill a large pot with water, turn it on to the highest setting to bring water to boil, add salt, and then cover to help water boil faster.
2. Put cubed potatoes into boiling water.
3. Turn down to medium-high on the stove, put the lid on the pot, but tilt it so steam can escape.
4. Boil for 35 minutes.
5. Poke with a fork to check that the potatoes are very soft.
6. Strain and transfer back to the pot.

Season with:

- □ 1 tablespoon salt
- □ 2 tablespoons oil and mix well

Curried Vegetable Sauté

- ☐ 2 heads of cauliflower florets chopped into half-inch pieces
- ☐ 2 bunches kale, stemmed, roughly chopped
- ☐ 1 cup water
- ☐ 1 teaspoon salt
- ☐ 1 tablespoon curry powder

1. Add the perfectly soft broccoli recipe to this recipe at the end so that the broccoli does not get overcooked with everything else.
2. Put cauliflower, salt, curry powder, and water into the pot.
3. Turn on to medium-high, cover, and let cook for 7 minutes.
4. Turn down to medium on the stove.
5. Add the kale and leave the cover off; cook for another 5 minutes, stirring occasionally.
6. Check that everything is fork tender.
7. Turn off the heat and then add the perfectly soft broccoli recipe to this recipe at the end so that the broccoli does not get overcooked with everything else.

Perfectly Soft Broccoli

☐ Begin with 3 broccoli crowns, cut into half-inch florets, chop into small pieces, and remove as much of the stem as possible!

☐ 1 teaspoon salt

☐ 1 teaspoon Italian herbs

1. Boil water and place broccoli into boiling water. Let the water come back to a boil, and then turn it down to medium-high to cook for 10 minutes.

2. Make sure to test for tenderness; poke with a fork. It needs to be fork tender and super soft—especially near the stem part of the broccoli floret.

3. Scoop the broccoli out into a bowl.

4. Toss with salt and Italian herbs.

Minced Cilantro

1. Remove the cilantro stems first.

2. Try to get the herbs minced as finely as possible, either with a knife, pizza cutter, or food processor.

3. Mix some into the curried vegetable sauté, and then save some for the top of the meals for garnish!

Power Paleo Meal Suggestions

Marinated Chicken Thighs with Italian Herbs with Curried Vegetable Sauté and Cubed Sweet Potatoes

8 meals with:

- ☐ 3/4 cup Marinated Chicken Thighs with Italian Herbs
- ☐ 3/4 cup Curried Vegetable Sauté
- ☐ 3/4 cup Cubed Sweet Potatoes
- ☐ 1 tablespoon fresh chopped cilantro on top

Salmon Caper Salad and Simple Poached Eggs with Curried Vegetable Sauté and Cubed Sweet Potatoes

4 meals with:

- ☐ 1/2 cup Salmon Caper Salad
- ☐ 2 Simple Poached Eggs
- ☐ 3/4 cup Curried Vegetable Sauté
- ☐ 3/4 cup Cubed Sweet Potatoes
- ☐ 1 tablespoon fresh chopped cilantro on top

Paleo Ethnic Pot Pie with Baked Herbed Ground Meat, Curried Vegetable Sauté, and Cubed Sweet Potatoes

4 meals with:

- □ 1/2 cup Baked Herbed Ground Meat (freeze the rest)
- □ 3/4 cup Curried Vegetable Sauté
- □ 3/4 cup Cubed Sweet Potatoes, mashed on top.
- □ 1 tablespoon fresh chopped cilantro on top

1. Create a pie formation with ground meat on the bottom, then vegetables, and then mashed sweet potatoes on top.
2. You can use a potato masher, spatula, or even just a spoon to mash the potatoes.
3. Freeze any leftovers.

Chapter Seven:
Putting It All Together: A Holistic Approach to Aging Well

As we embark on the journey of aging, there is an inherent desire to not just live longer but to live better. The pursuit of longevity and well-being has led many to explore various avenues, including supplements and vitamins, physical exercises, and wellness practices. In this final chapter, we delve into the essential components of a holistic approach to aging well, providing valuable insights on how to make informed decisions for a fulfilling and happy life.

We uncover the world of supplements and vitamins, their potential role in longevity, and how to navigate the vast market to choose the best options. We will explore the scientific evidence supporting specific supplements and their potential benefits in maintaining health and vitality as we age. Additionally, we explore how simple wellness practices, such as mindful breathing and stretching, can be seamlessly integrated into daily life to improve overall well-being.

By the end of this chapter, you will have gained a comprehensive understanding of how to choose quality supplements and vitamins, how to incorporate chair exercises and wellness practices into everyday life, and the profound benefits of embracing aging with optimism and grace. Armed with this knowledge, you can confidently embark on a holistic journey toward aging well, empowering yourself to lead a fulfilling life that thrives in all aspects of health and happiness. Let's dive in!

Supplements and Vitamins for Healthy Aging

Let me begin by saying that not everyone requires supplements as a vital part of their diet. Most people can meet all their nutritional needs simply by consuming an overall nutritious, balanced diet. Supplements are intended to help you get better results after you already have a solid eating plan and understand proper nutrition. Use supplements as intended: as supplementary substances to your nutrition and exercise, rather than relying on them solely. They shouldn't substitute for or replace a healthy diet, exercise, and other healthy habits and practices.

Below is a list of supplements that are well-suited for seniors:

1. Multivitamins

Multivitamins are one of the most popular supplements, providing a comprehensive blend of essential vitamins and minerals. These supplements often contain vitamins A, C, D, E, K, and various B vitamins, as well as essential minerals like zinc, magnesium, and selenium. Multivitamins can support various bodily functions, including immune health, bone strength, cognitive function, and energy production.

While obtaining vitamins and minerals from whole foods is preferable, it is often challenging for some people to meet all the recommended daily dosages and vitamin requirements. In such cases, multivitamins can serve as a supplement to fill in the gaps. However, it should be used as additional support and not as a justification to consume unhealthy foods. The primary focus should still be on maintaining a balanced and nutritious diet.

2. Omega-3 Fatty Acids

Omega-3 fatty acids are essential for maintaining good health—just as you've seen. However, our bodies cannot produce them on their own. Therefore, it's crucial to include them in our diet, as they cannot be synthesized internally. Unfortunately, many people do not regularly consume rich sources of omega-3 like salmon, mackerel, and tuna, making it challenging to meet the recommended intake of these vital nutrients. Consequently, supplementation has become a popular choice to fill this nutritional gap.

But try your best to get omega-3 fatty acids from your meals. This is because sources of these fatty acids, like oily fish, walnuts, and chia seeds, not only provide valuable omega-3s but also serve as excellent sources of high-quality protein.

It is advisable to include fish in your meal plan and ensure an adequate intake. However, if it's challenging to consume enough fish in your diet, you can consider relying on reputable and trustworthy supplement brands as a viable alternative.

3. Probiotics

Having a healthy gut has a significant impact on various aspects of our well-being, including inflammation, mental clarity, weight management, sleep quality, and even emotional well-being. The state of our gut is intricately linked to almost every aspect of our overall health. Probiotics are live microorganisms that promote a healthy balance of gut bacteria.

As with most nutrients, the ideal way to obtain probiotics is by consuming them through the foods you eat. You can increase your probiotic intake by incorporating fermented foods into your diet, such as yogurt, kefir, kombucha, refrigerated sauerkraut, kimchi, tempeh, and miso. However, if you're unable to consume these foods, considering a supplement can be a reasonable option. Probiotic supplements can help restore and maintain a diverse gut microbiota, improving digestion and supporting immune function.

Studies suggest that supplements of probiotics—the "good" bacteria residing in your digestive system that help keep "bad" bacteria in check—may have the potential to counteract age-related changes in gut microbiota, enhance immune health, and promote healthy digestion (Hutchinson et al., 2021).

4. Protein Powders

Protein powders, such as whey, casein, or plant-based options like pea or soy protein, can provide a concentrated source of protein to support muscle health.

Protein powders can be easily incorporated into smoothies or other beverages, making them an accessible way to boost protein intake, particularly for older adults who may have difficulty consuming enough protein from whole foods.

5. Calcium and Vitamin D

Calcium and vitamin D work hand in hand to support bone health. Vitamin D enhances calcium absorption and aids in maintaining proper levels of calcium in the blood. While calcium is found in dairy products and leafy greens, vitamin D is primarily synthesized through exposure to sunlight. However, many adults may have reduced sun exposure, making supplementation necessary.

6. Collagen

Collagen is the most abundant protein in the body, providing structural support to the skin, bones, tendons, and ligaments.

Collagen supplements, derived from animal sources like bovine or marine collagen, have gained popularity for their potential to support skin elasticity, joint health, and overall connective tissue function. A 2019 research review published in the Journal of Drugs in Dermatology concluded that taking oral collagen supplements helps increase skin density, hydration, and elasticity (Choi et al., 2019).

How to Choose Quality Supplements

With an abundance of options available on the market, the task of selecting quality supplements can be overwhelming. However, armed with the right knowledge and criteria, you can make informed choices that optimize the benefits of supplementation while ensuring safety and efficacy. Here are some tips and essential factors to consider when choosing quality supplements:

- *Look for Reputable Brands with Third-Party Testing and Certifications*: Choosing supplements from reputable brands is crucial to ensuring product quality and safety. Reputable companies often invest in third-party testing by independent laboratories, which verifies the accuracy of label claims and ensures that the products meet quality standards. Additionally, certifications from recognized organizations, such as Good Manufacturing Practices (GMP) and the National Sanitation Foundation (NSF International), provide further assurance of a brand's commitment to quality.

- *Read Labels for Transparent Ingredient Lists and Proper Dosage Information*: Transparent and comprehensive ingredient lists are essential for consumers to make informed choices about the supplements they are considering. Look for clear information about the active ingredients, their sources, and any additional excipients or fillers used in the product. Furthermore, proper dosage information is critical to ensure that the supplement provides the intended health benefits without the risk of overconsumption.

- *Choose Supplements with Bioavailable Forms of Nutrients for Optimal Absorption*: Bioavailability refers to the degree to which the nutrients in a supplement can be absorbed and utilized by the body. Opt for supplements that contain bioavailable forms of nutrients, as these are more readily absorbed, making them more effective in supporting overall health.

- *Consider Your Specific Needs and Consult with a Healthcare Professional*: Each individual's nutritional needs are unique, and supplements should be selected based on personal health goals, age, gender, and lifestyle.

Consulting with a qualified healthcare professional, such as a doctor or a registered dietitian, can provide personalized recommendations and assure you to make purchases with confidence.

- *Avoid Supplements with Excessive Fillers, Additives, or Unnecessary Ingredients*: Some supplements may contain unnecessary additives, fillers, or artificial ingredients that can detract from the overall quality of the product. Look for supplements with minimal and clean ingredient lists to ensure that you are getting the most beneficial nutrients without unnecessary additives.

- *Research the Manufacturing Processes and Quality Control Standards of the Brand*: Investigate the manufacturing processes and quality control standards of the brand to ensure that the supplements are produced in a safe and controlled environment. Brands that prioritize quality control are more likely to provide consistent and reliable products.

- *Check for Expiration Dates to Ensure Freshness and Potency*: Expired supplements may lose their potency and effectiveness, rendering them less beneficial. Always check for expiration dates on supplement packaging to ensure that you are consuming a fresh and potent product.

- *Look for Supplements That Are Free from Common Allergens If Necessary*: Individuals with allergies or sensitivities should seek supplements that are free from common allergens, such as gluten, dairy, soy, or nuts. Allergen-free supplements are especially important for those with known allergies or intolerances to avoid adverse reactions.

- *Consider the Form of the Supplement for Preference*: Supplements come in various forms, including capsules, tablets, liquids, and powders. Consider your personal preference and any specific requirements, such as ease of swallowing or digestibility, when choosing the form of the supplement.

- *Evaluate Customer Reviews and Testimonials for Insights on Product Effectiveness*: Customer reviews and testimonials can offer valuable insights into the effectiveness and quality of a supplement. Reading about other users' experiences can provide a more comprehensive understanding of the product's benefits and potential drawbacks.

- *Ensure the Supplement Meets Regulatory Standards and Guidelines*: Look for supplements that comply with relevant regulatory standards and guidelines, such as those set by the U.S. Food and Drug Administration (FDA) or equivalent regulatory bodies in other countries. Regulatory compliance ensures that the product meets safety and quality requirements.

Choosing quality supplements is a critical aspect of incorporating nutritional support into a healthy lifestyle. If all of the above tips are considered when purchasing your supplements, they can help you make the right choice. With the right approach, high-quality supplements can become powerful allies in enhancing your life and achieving long-term health and wellness.

Incorporating Chair Exercises into Daily Life

One of the key factors in successfully incorporating chair exercises into daily life is to schedule regular exercise time. Just like any other important commitment, setting aside dedicated time for exercise helps create consistency and ensures that physical activity becomes an integral part of our daily routine. Whether it's in the morning, afternoon, or evening, having a specific time slot for chair exercises can help us prioritize our health and well-being.

Before commencing any exercise routine, it is essential to prepare the body with gentle warm-up stretches. Warm-up stretches increase blood flow to the muscles, reduce the risk of injury, and enhance flexibility, making them crucial for seniors engaging in chair exercises. Incorporating warm-up stretches ensures a safe and effective workout session. If you have time, you can do the first routine in Chapter Three and then move on to Chapter Four and/or Chapter Five, and that will give you a nice warm-up that flows into some more active poses.

For seniors who enjoy watching television, incorporating chair exercises during TV commercials or while watching shows can be an effective strategy. During commercial breaks or slower moments in a show, seniors can take advantage of the time by engaging in simple chair exercises.

Chair exercises can be further enhanced by incorporating light weights or resistance to increase the intensity of the workout. You can use traditional dumbbells or even everyday household items like water bottles or canned goods, which can serve as effective makeshift weights. This simple addition adds resistance, helping to strengthen muscles and improve endurance without the need for specialized equipment.

Involving a friend or family member in your exercise journey can be a source of great motivation and support. Seniors can encourage a loved one to join them in their chair exercise routine, creating a shared fitness experience that fosters camaraderie and encouragement. Exercising with a partner provides an opportunity for social interaction and accountability. Seniors can challenge and motivate each other, celebrate achievements together, and provide encouragement during the workout sessions.

As seniors become more comfortable with chair exercises, gradually increasing the duration and intensity of the exercises over time is essential to continuously challenge the body and see progress. Incrementally adding more repetitions or extending the exercise duration allows seniors to build strength and stamina at a comfortable pace without feeling overwhelmed.

Adding a dose of entertainment to chair exercises can make the experience more enjoyable and engaging. Listening to music with a steady beat can serve as a natural rhythm for seniors to follow during their exercises, turning the workout into a lively dance-like activity. Alternatively, audiobooks or podcasts can provide mental stimulation and distraction, keeping you mentally engaged and entertained during your exercise sessions. This enjoyable addition to the routine can make chair exercises something to look forward to each day.

Consistency is paramount for reaping the full benefits of chair exercises. Seniors can use various methods to stay on track with their daily workouts. Setting reminders on your smartphones or using calendars can serve as gentle nudges to engage in chair exercises regularly. Fitness tracking apps or wearable devices can be valuable tools for monitoring exercise progress and staying motivated. These apps can record workout sessions, track steps taken, and even provide virtual rewards or badges for achieving fitness milestones, making the exercise journey more engaging and rewarding.

As with any exercise regimen, it is essential to listen to our bodies and modify exercises as needed to accommodate any physical limitations or health concerns. Chair exercises can be adapted to suit individual fitness levels and needs. If a particular exercise causes discomfort or strain, we can explore alternative movements that target the same muscle groups with less impact. Consulting with a healthcare professional or a fitness instructor who specializes in senior exercise can provide valuable guidance on safe and effective modifications.

Embarking on a fitness journey can sometimes feel overwhelming, particularly for seniors. Celebrating each step of progress, no matter how small, can serve as a powerful motivator. Recognizing and celebrating even the tiniest achievements can boost motivation and self-confidence, encouraging you to continue your chair exercise routine with enthusiasm. Rather than striving for perfection, you should focus on individual progress and improvement over time. Setting realistic and achievable goals allows us to measure our advancement and recognize the positive impact of our efforts on our overall health and well-being.

Incorporating chair exercises into your daily life offers a valuable opportunity for you to maintain an active and healthy lifestyle. Chair exercises offer a flexible and accessible way for you to maintain mobility and flexibility and experience the joy of a healthy and fulfilling life.

Incorporating Wellness Practices into Daily Life

As the golden years approach, embracing wellness practices becomes increasingly vital for maintaining a fulfilling and vibrant life. Wellness encompasses a holistic approach to health, encompassing physical, mental, and emotional well-being. By incorporating wellness practices into your daily life, you can cultivate a lifestyle that supports your overall health and happiness. Here is a comprehensive range of wellness practices and strategies that you can adopt to enhance your well-being:

- *Set Aside Dedicated Time for Wellness Practices Each Day*

Creating dedicated time for wellness practices is an essential step in nurturing our physical, mental, and emotional well-being. By setting aside a specific time each day, we demonstrate a commitment to our well-being and ensure that wellness practices become an integral part of our routines.

Whether it's starting the day with a few moments of meditation, going for a walk, or practicing yoga before bedtime, having dedicated time allows us to focus solely on nurturing ourselves. Consistency in carving out this time fosters a sense of balance and empowerment as we prioritize our health and happiness.

- *Start with Simple Practices like Deep Breathing or Mindfulness Meditation*

Embarking on a wellness journey can feel overwhelming, especially for those who are new to these practices. Starting with simple techniques, such as deep breathing or mindfulness meditation, provides a gentle introduction to the world of wellness.

Deep breathing exercises help us relax, reduce stress, and improve focus. This practice can be done anywhere and requires no special equipment. Mindfulness meditation cultivates present-moment awareness and helps us let go of distractions, leading to a calmer and more centered state of mind.

By beginning with these uncomplicated practices, we gradually build the foundation for more complex wellness modalities and pave the way for a more profound sense of well-being.

- *Create a Calming Environment by Decluttering Your House and Adding Soothing Elements*

Our physical environment significantly impacts our mental and emotional well-being. A cluttered and chaotic space can contribute to feelings of stress and unease, while a clean and organized environment promotes a sense of calm and relaxation.

By decluttering our homes and adding soothing elements, such as soft lighting, plants, or calming scents, we create a haven for our minds to unwind and rejuvenate. Seeking help can make the process easier and more enjoyable. Depending on your budget, you can get help from house cleaners, professional organizers, or even just your friends and family.

- *Incorporate Wellness Practices into Morning or Bedtime Routines for Consistency*

Wellness practices are most effective when integrated into daily routines. Incorporating wellness practices into our morning and bedtime routines ensures that they become consistent habits. A morning wellness practice sets a positive tone for the day ahead, while an evening practice aids in winding down and preparing for a restful sleep.

Morning routines may include going for a walk, gratitude journaling, or a few moments of quiet reflection. Bedtime routines could involve relaxation techniques such as guided meditation or reading a calming book. These rituals anchor us to self-care and establish a sense of structure, promoting overall well-being throughout the day.

- *Use Smartphone Apps or Guided Meditation Recordings for Support and Guidance*

In our technology-driven world, smartphones can be valuable tools for supporting our wellness practices. Smartphone apps and guided meditation recordings offer convenient access to guided sessions and valuable resources. Whether we're looking to meditate, practice yoga, or engage in breathing exercises, these apps provide step-by-step guidance and motivation. Some apps also offer reminders, allowing us to stay consistent in our wellness journey despite our busy schedules.

- *Experiment with Different Practices to Find What Resonates with You*

Wellness is a deeply personal journey, and what works for one individual may not resonate with another. To discover the practices that align with our unique preferences and needs, it is essential to experiment with different modalities. From yoga and tai chi to journaling and dance, exploring various wellness practices allows us to uncover those that bring us the most joy, relaxation, and contentment. Trying different practices can be an adventure of self-discovery, enabling us to tailor our wellness routine to suit our individuality.

- *Take Short Breaks during the Day for Quick Mindfulness or Stretching Sessions*

Taking short breaks for quick mindfulness or stretching sessions can make a significant difference in our well-being. These breaks provide us with a moment to pause, reset, and recharge, improving focus and productivity. Incorporating mindfulness breaks throughout the day can help reduce stress and promote mental clarity. Stretching sessions can alleviate physical tension and improve circulation, contributing to a healthier body and mind.

- *Practice Gratitude by Reflecting on Positive Aspects of Your Life*

Practicing gratitude is a transformative wellness practice that cultivates a positive mindset and enhances our overall sense of well-being. By taking time each day to reflect on the things we are thankful for, we shift our focus from what we lack to what we have.

Keeping a gratitude journal, where we write down the things we appreciate, allows us to revisit these positive aspects whenever we need a boost of positivity. This practice helps us develop a mindset of abundance and fosters contentment with the present moment.

- *Engage in Physical Activities You Enjoy, Such as Walking or Gardening*

At this point, you already know that physical activity is an integral part of a healthy lifestyle and contributes significantly to our well-being. Engaging in physical activities we enjoy not only benefits our bodies but also uplifts our spirits and brings joy.

Whether it's going for a walk in nature, dancing to our favorite music, or tending to a garden, these activities elevate our mood, reduce stress, and improve our overall physical health. Embracing movement as a form of self-expression and pleasure transforms exercise from a chore into a source of happiness.

- *Prioritize Self-Care by Nourishing Your Body with Healthy Food and Hydration*

Nourishing our bodies with healthy food and staying hydrated is a fundamental aspect of self-care. Proper nutrition provides essential nutrients for our bodies to function optimally, supporting overall health and well-being. A diet rich in fruits, vegetables, lean proteins, and healthy fats nourishes our bodies and provides energy for our daily activities. Staying hydrated by drinking an adequate amount of water is vital for maintaining optimal bodily functions.

- *Plan and Prepare Balanced Meals in Advance for Convenience*

Planning and preparing balanced meals in advance can save time and make healthy eating more accessible. When we plan our meals ahead of time, we are less likely to resort to unhealthy options due to time constraints or a lack of preparation. By preparing meals that include a variety of nutrients, we ensure that our bodies receive the necessary fuel to thrive. Planning meals can also be a creative and enjoyable process as we explore new recipes and flavors. There are also many meal plan services offering healthy options these days for those who have less time and the resources to do that. Or you can engage your family and friends to prepare meals together, as stated in the next point!

- *Involve Family or Friends in Meal Planning and Cooking Together*

Mealtimes can be a wonderful opportunity for social connection. Involving family or friends in meal planning and cooking fosters a sense of togetherness and enriches the dining experience. Sharing the process of preparing meals with loved ones creates bonds and strengthens connections. Cooking together can be a fun and rewarding activity, allowing us to share our favorite dishes, learn new recipes, and enjoy each other's company. Moreover, involving others in meal planning can provide us with diverse perspectives and ideas for healthier and more exciting meals.

- *Take Time to Enjoy Meals Mindfully, Savoring Each Bite*

Mindful eating encourages you to savor each meal and fully engage with the sensory experience of eating. When we eat mindfully, we focus on the taste, texture, and aroma of the food. By slowing down and savoring each bite, we become more attuned to our body's hunger and fullness cues, leading to better digestion and a more balanced relationship with food.

Mindful eating also encourages us to notice how different foods make us feel, helping us make healthier choices that support our well-being. By appreciating the nourishment that food provides and being mindful of the pleasure of eating, we foster a positive and conscious approach to nutrition.

- *Seek Support from Community Groups or Wellness Classes for Encouragement*

Social support is a powerful catalyst for progress in your life's endeavors. Feeling connected to a supportive community is vital for our mental and emotional well-being. Seeking out community groups or participating in wellness classes can provide a sense of belonging, encouragement, and accountability on our journey. Community groups, such as fitness classes or meditation circles, offer opportunities to connect with like-minded individuals who share similar goals. Being part of a supportive community can motivate us to stay committed to our wellness practices and celebrate our achievements together.

Engaging with others in a healthy setting also offers valuable opportunities for learning and growth. Sharing experiences and insights within a community allows us to gain new perspectives and approaches to wellness that we may not have considered on our own. In addition to in-person community groups, online platforms also offer virtual communities centered around well-being. Participating in online forums, social media groups, or wellness apps can provide a sense of connection and support, even from the comfort of our own homes.

Incorporating these practices into our daily routines empowers us to lead balanced and centered lives where self-care and community connection become integral aspects of our well-being. By nurturing mindfulness, relaxation, and community engagement, we pave the way for a happier, healthier, and more fulfilling life.

- *Disconnect from Screens and Engaging in Activities That Promote Relaxation*

In the last point, digital tools were mentioned as a form of supporting connection with your community; however, this should be used in moderation. In the digital age, screen time can be overwhelming and disruptive to overall well-being. Incorporating moments of screen-free relaxation is essential for recharging our minds and promoting emotional well-being.

By disconnecting from screens, we create space for activities that promote relaxation and stress relief. Engaging in hobbies like reading, drawing, or spending time in nature allows us to be fully present in the moment, free from the demands of technology.

Furthermore, screen-free relaxation can enhance our sleep quality. Disconnecting from screens before bedtime reduces exposure to blue light, which can disrupt our sleep patterns. Engaging in calming activities instead prepares our bodies for rest and ensures a more restorative sleep.

Embracing the Process and Enjoying the Journey

Life is a remarkable journey filled with experiences that shape us into who we are. As time passes, we gain wisdom and life experiences that become invaluable assets in our pursuit of happiness and fulfillment. Embracing this process of growth and self-discovery is essential, especially as we age. As one enters their senior years, there is a unique opportunity to embrace aging and find joy in the evolving self.

Life's journey is an accumulation of experiences, and with age comes a wealth of wisdom. The knowledge gained through the years becomes a guiding light, enabling us to make wiser decisions and offer valuable insights to others. Embracing this wisdom allows us to appreciate the growth that comes with each chapter of life and celebrate the journey we have traveled.

Central to this journey is self-acceptance and cultivating a positive self-image. As the years go by, physical appearances may change, and societal expectations may evolve. However, embracing our uniqueness and valuing ourselves for who we are are powerful acts of self-love. By practicing self-acceptance, we can navigate life with confidence and grace, free from the burden of comparison or self-doubt.

Taking care of our physical and emotional well-being is essential to embracing the journey fully. Self-care is not a luxury but a necessity. Nourishing our bodies with nutritious foods, engaging in regular physical activity, and allowing ourselves time for rest and relaxation are fundamental to maintaining a healthy and balanced lifestyle. Additionally, nurturing our emotional well-being through mindfulness and seeking support when needed fosters inner peace and resilience.

Life is meant to be enjoyed, and engaging in activities that bring joy and fulfillment is an integral part of the journey. Whether it is pursuing hobbies, spending time in nature, or connecting with loved ones, these activities enrich our lives and bring a profound sense of happiness.

Our relationships play a crucial role in our well-being. Surrounding ourselves with positive and supportive individuals fosters a sense of belonging and strengthens our emotional resilience. These relationships serve as pillars of support, guiding us through life's challenges and celebrating our triumphs.

A growth mindset is the key to continuous personal development. Maintaining curiosity and an openness to learning allows us to explore new interests and engage in intellectual pursuits. The journey of learning is never-ending, and each discovery enriches our lives with new perspectives and knowledge.

Practicing gratitude and appreciating the present moment is a transformative practice. By focusing on what we have and expressing gratitude for life's blessings, we shift our perspective to one of abundance and contentment. Gratitude grounds us in the present, enabling us to savor life's joys and find peace amidst the chaos.

Breaking free from societal expectations and embracing our unique path is liberating. Each individual's journey is distinctive, and there is beauty in the diversity of life experiences. By letting go of external pressures and living life authentically, we discover a sense of freedom and empowerment.

On this journey, it is essential to celebrate our milestones and achievements, regardless of their size. Each success, big or small, represents progress and growth. Recognizing and celebrating our accomplishments adds a sense of fulfillment and motivation to continue pushing forward.

Finding beauty in the journey itself is a profound mindset to adopt. Embracing the ever-evolving self and acknowledging the growth we experience throughout life is a testament to our resilience. Each phase of life contributes to the masterpiece of who we are.

Change is inevitable, and our ability to adapt is crucial. Embracing change as a natural part of life enables us to navigate transitions with grace and courage. Rather than fearing change, we can view it as an opportunity for growth and new beginnings.

Finally, cultivating a sense of purpose and finding meaning in each day infuses our journey with depth and significance. Our purpose may evolve as we age, and discovering meaning in daily activities brings fulfillment and a profound sense of satisfaction.

Embracing the aging process and enjoying the journey is an art of self-discovery and growth. Each day presents an opportunity to embrace the beauty of life's ever-evolving tapestry, celebrating the journey we have walked and the growth that lies ahead. By embracing the process, we can fully enjoy the journey and savor each moment, creating a life that is rich in experiences, joy, and profound fulfillment.

Will You Spare a Moment to Help Someone Else?

I'm excited for the future that you have ahead of you – and this is your chance to help someone else discover the power of chair exercises too.

Simply by sharing your thoughts on this book and a little about your own experience, you'll show new readers the route to a life-changing journey – and share a healthy dose of inspiration in the process.

I know we can make a huge difference to many more people – thank you so much for your help with this.

Please leave a review on Amazon to help others find this content!

https://www.amazon.com/review/create-review/?asin=B0CM6XYT4L

Conclusion

This book has illuminated a path toward enhancing not just physical health but also nurturing the spirit of independence and overall well-being.

Throughout these pages, we've explored the myriad benefits of chair exercises and movement routines. Through these 10-minute workouts, you will rediscover your independence and reclaim your sense of self. Each exercise serves as a powerful reminder of your inherent capability to adapt, grow, and thrive. As you commit to this journey, you will witness your confidence soar, eradicating any doubts about your ability to conquer the challenges life presents.

The advantages of this book extend beyond physical well-being. Within these pages, you discovered essential health tips for holistic living and everyday vitality. By adopting a holistic approach to your well-being, you will experience a profound enhancement of your mental and emotional health.

The important message resonates clearly: By incorporating chair exercises and holistic wellness practices into daily life, seniors can enrich their lives. The magic lies in the fusion of these elements—from seated mobility exercises that cultivate flexibility to balance-enhancing routines that instill stability and from mindful eating to embracing nutrient-dense foods. Understanding the science of habit formation, we've explored various strategies and methods for cultivating good habits. These tools enable us to create positive habits and break free from undesirable ones, leading to long-lasting results.

We've journeyed into the realm of phytonutrients and the rainbow-hued palette of nutrition, and we've explored the Paleo diet. The role of consistency, the power of supplements and vitamins in supporting healthy aging, and how to choose quality options also found their place in our exploration.

As we conclude, remember that this is a journey, not a destination. Embrace the process, for it is within the journey itself that transformation takes root. By prioritizing chair exercises and holistic wellness practices, you can sculpt a life of vitality, mobility, and balance.

Let your journey toward improved health and well-being begin now! Your future self will thank you for this investment in your flourishing. Remember, it's never too late to start, and every small step counts toward a healthier future.

Stay committed, be consistent, and enjoy the journey of self-improvement and well-being. Together, let's age with strength, grace, and vitality. Here's to a vibrant and healthy life ahead!

References

American Holistic Health Association. (2023, July 30). *Principles of Holistic Medicine – Article - American Holistic Health Association.* https://ahha.org/principles-holistic-medicine-article/.

Åsgård, R., Rytter, E., Basu, S., Abramsson-Zetterberg, L., Möller, L., & Vessby, B. (2007). High intake of fruit and vegetables is related to low oxidative stress and inflammation in a group of patients with type 2 diabetes. *Scandinavian Journal of Food & Nutrition, 51*(4), 149–158. https://doi.org/10.1080/17482970701737285.

Bahamondes, M. A., Valdés, C., & Moncada, G. (2021). Effect of omega-3 on painful symptoms of patients with osteoarthritis of the synovial joints: systematic review and meta-analysis. *Oral Surgery, Oral Medicine, Oral Pathology, and Oral Radiology, 132*(3), 297–306. https://doi.org/10.1016/j.oooo.2021.01.020.

Bailey, R. L., Jun, S., Murphy, L., Green, R., Gahche, J. J., Dwyer, J., Potischman, N., McCabe, G. P., & Miller, J. W. (2020). High folic acid or folate combined with low vitamin B-12 status: potential but inconsistent association with cognitive function in a nationally representative cross-sectional sample of US older adults participating in the NHANES. *The American Journal of Clinical Nutrition, 112*(6), 1547–1557. https://doi.org/10.1093/ajcn/nqaa239.

Barone, M., Turroni, S., Rampelli, S., Soverini, M., D'Amico, F., Biagi, E., Brigidi, P., Troiani, E., & Candela, M. (2019). Gut microbiome response to a modern Paleolithic diet in a Western lifestyle context. *PLOS ONE, 14*(8), e0220619. https://doi.org/10.1371/journal.pone.0220619.

Benedetti, M. G., Furlini, G., Zati, A., & Mauro, G. L. (2018). The effectiveness of physical exercise on bone density in osteoporotic patients. *BioMed Research International, 2018*, 1–10. https://doi.org/10.1155/2018/4840531.

Bhg-Admin. (2023, June 29). *The Many Benefits of Walking for Seniors - Bethesda Health Group.* Bethesda Health Group. https://bethesdahealth.org/blog/2021/03/25/the-many-benefits-of-walking-for-seniors/.

Bhirani, R. (2021, October 19). *Add phytonutrients to your diet to fight and prevent health issues.* Healthshots. https://www.healthshots.com/healthy-eating/nutrition/what-are-phytonutrients-and-what-are-their-health-benefits/.

Bilazzo, K. (2017, December 31). *8 Ways to Incorporate Healthy Eating Habits into Your Daily Routine.* Diana Gregory Outreach Services. https://dianagregory.com/8-ways-to-incorporate-healthy-eating-habits-into-your-daily-routine/.

Billingsley, H., & Carbone, S. (2018). The phytonutrient potential of the Mediterranean diet in patients at high cardiovascular risk: an in-depth review of the PREDIMED. *Nutrition & Diabetes, 8*(1). https://doi.org/10.1038/s41387-018-0025-1.

Bodybuilding.com. (n.d.). *Standing hip extension | Exercise Videos & Guides | Bodybuilding.com.* https://www.bodybuilding.com/exercises/leg-lift.

Brar, F. (2022, June 25). This 76-Year-Old Fitness Fanatic Is Defying Expectations On Every Level. *Shape.* https://www.shape.com/lifestyle/mind-and-body/joan-macdonald-73-year-old-fitness-fanatic.

Bulló, M., Juanola-Falgarona, M., Hernández-Alonso, P., & Salas-Salvadó, J. (2015). Nutrition attributes and health effects of pistachio nuts. *British Journal of Nutrition, 113*(S2), S79–S93. https://doi.org/10.1017/s0007114514003250.

Cantkier, L. (2018). Which foods contain the most phytonutrients? *University Health News.* https://universityhealthnews.com/daily/nutrition/foods-contain-phytonutrients/.

Carbone, J. W., & Pasiakos, S. M. (2019). Dietary Protein and Muscle Mass: Translating science to application and health benefit. *Nutrients, 11*(5), 1136. https://doi.org/10.3390/nu11051136.

CaroMont Health. (2023, January 18). Seven easy ways to include exercise in your daily routine. *CaroMont Health.* https://caromonthealth.org/news/seven-easy-ways-to-include-exercise-in-your-daily-routine/.

Carr, A. C., & Maggini, S. (2017). Vitamin C and immune function. *Nutrients, 9*(11), 1211. https://doi.org/10.3390/nu9111211.

Chair seated shoulder circles Yoga | Yoga sequences, benefits, variations, and Sanskrit pronunciation | Tummee.com. (2017, October 15). Tummee.com. https://www.tummee.com/yoga-poses/chair-seated-shoulder-circles.

Chair torso circles Yoga | Yoga sequences, benefits, variations, and Sanskrit Pronunciation | Tummee.com. (2018, July 27). Tummee.com. https://www.tummee.com/yoga-poses/chair-torso-circles.

Chapman, N., Jacobs, R. J., & Braakhuis, A. (2018). Role of diet and food intake in age-related macular degeneration: a systematic review. *Clinical and Experimental Ophthalmology, 47*(1), 106–127. https://doi.org/10.1111/ceo.13343.

Choi, F., Sung, C., Juhasz, M., & Mesinkovsk, N. A. (2019). Oral Collagen Supplementation: A Systematic Review of Dermatological Applications. *PubMed, 18*(1), 9–16. https://pubmed.ncbi.nlm.nih.gov/30681787.

Cicero, K. (2023). The Benefits I've Noticed From Tracking My Habits for 3 Years. *Wit & Delight | Designing a Life Well-Lived*. https://witanddelight.com/2022/09/tracking-my-habits-benefits/.

Clear, J. (2020, February 4). *How to break a bad habit (and replace it with a good one)*. James Clear. https://jamesclear.com/how-to-break-a-bad-habit.

Cole, G. M., Ma, Q., & Frautschy, S. A. (2009). Omega-3 fatty acids and dementia. *Prostaglandins Leukotrienes and Essential Fatty Acids, 81*(2–3), 213–221. https://doi.org/10.1016/j.plefa.2009.05.015.

Consistency is the key to breaking bad habits and forming good ones. (2015, January 17). *Entrepreneur*. https://www.entrepreneur.com/living/consistency-is-the-key-to-breaking-bad-habits-and-forming/241635.

Contreras, J., Alcázar-Valle, M., Lugo-Cervantes, E., Luna-Vital, D. A., & Mojica, L. (2023). Mexican Native Black Bean Anthocyanin-Rich Extracts Modulate Biological Markers Associated with Inflammation. *Pharmaceuticals, 16*(6), 874. https://doi.org/10.3390/ph16060874.

Cooper, B. B. (2015, May 12). Why you should be tracking your habits (and how to do it well). *Lifehacker*. https://lifehacker.com/why-you-should-be-tracking-your-habits-and-how-to-do-i-1702100388.

Daily Mail. (2010, September 14). Study finds people with lots of friends live 3.7 years more than those who are isolated. *Mail Online*. https://www.dailymail.co.uk/news/article-1311676/Study-finds-people-lots-friends-live-3-7-years-isolated.html.

Damianne. (2023, February 25). *Be Consistent to build a New Habit - Changes BIG and small*. Changes BIG and Small. https://changesbigandsmall.com/be-consistent-to-build-a-new-habit/.

Dancer Pose with Chair Yoga (Natarajasana with chair) | Yoga sequences, benefits, variations, and Sanskrit pronunciation | Tummee.com. (2019, March 12). Tummee. com. https://www.tummee.com/yoga-poses/dancer-pose-with-chair.

Deepika, & Maurya, P. K. (2022). Health Benefits of Quercetin in Age-Related Diseases. *Molecules, 27*(8), 2498. https://doi.org/10.3390/molecules27082498.

Del Moral, A. a. M., & Fortique, F. (2019). Omega-3 fatty acids and cognitive decline: a systematic review. *Nutricion Hospitalaria.* https://doi.org/10.20960/nh.02496.

DelfinKim, D. (2023, March 12). *10 health benefits of a paleo diet.* Health & Detox & Vitamins. https://supernutritious.net/10-health-benefits-of-a-paleo-diet/?utm_source.

Dienstmann, G. (2021). Habit Cues. *Mindful Self-Discipline.* https://www.mindfulselfdiscipline.com/habit-cues/.

Dighriri, I. M., Alsubaie, A. M., Hakami, F. M., Hamithi, D. M., Alshekh, M. M., Khobrani, F. A., Dalak, F. E., Hakami, A. A., Alsueaadi, E. H., Alsaawi, L. S., Alshammari, S. F., Alqahtani, A. S., Alawi, I. A., Aljuaid, A. A., & Tawhari, M. Q. (2022). Effects of omega-3 polyunsaturated fatty acids on brain functions: a systematic review. *Cureus.* https://doi.org/10.7759/cureus.30091.

Donini, L. M., Poggiogalle, E., Piredda, M., Pinto, A., Barbagallo, M., Cucinotta, D., & Sergi, G. (2013). Anorexia and eating patterns in the elderly. *PLOS ONE, 8*(5), e63539. https://doi.org/10.1371/journal.pone.0063539.

Downward facing dog pose variation both knees bent chair yoga (Adho Mukha Svanasana variation both knees bent chair) | Yoga sequences, benefits, variations, and Sanskrit Pronunciation | Tummee.com. (2018, September 9). Tummee.com. https://www.tummee.com/yoga-poses/downward-facing-dog-pose-variation-both-knees-bent-chair.

Dyck, G. J. B., Raj, P., Zieroth, S., Dyck, J. R., & Ezekowitz, J. A. (2019). The Effects of Resveratrol in Patients with Cardiovascular Disease and Heart Failure: A Narrative Review. *International Journal of Molecular Sciences, 20*(4), 904. https://doi.org/10.3390/ijms20040904.

Evans, J. P., & Johnson, E. J. (2010). The role of phytonutrients in skin health. *Nutrients, 2*(8), 903–928. https://doi.org/10.3390/nu20809033.

Forni, C., Facchiano, F., Bartoli, M., Pieretti, S., Facchiano, A., D'Arcangelo, D., Norelli, S., Valle, G., Nisini, R., Beninati, S., Tabolacci, C., & Jadeja, R. N. (2019). Beneficial Role of Phytochemicals on Oxidative Stress and Age-Related Diseases. *BioMed Research International, 2019*, 1–16. https://doi.org/10.1155/2019/8748253.

Fu, T., & Shen, L. (2022). Ergothioneine as a natural phytonutrient against oxidative Stress-Related diseases. *Frontiers in Pharmacology, 13*. https://doi.org/10.3389/fphar.2022.850813.

Fusco, D., Colloca, G., Lo Monaco, M. R., & Cesari, M. (2007). Effects of phytonutrient supplementation on the aging process. *DOAJ (DOAJ: Directory of Open Access Journals)*. https://doaj.org/article/fdf977e2dfb-6417fb4f98538e8fdead8.

Gaillard, L. (2022). 4 Easy chair exercises for Seniors [Video]. *AlgaeCal*. https://blog.algaecal.com/chair-exercises-for-seniors/

Ganesan, K., & Xu, B. (2017). Polyphenol-Rich lentils and their health promoting effects. *International Journal of Molecular Sciences, 18*(11), 2390. https://doi.org/10.3390/ijms18112390.

GDPR support. (n.d.). https://www.ajc.com/lifestyles/study-live-long-life-you-should-embrace-getting-older/b3o%20WB74CzB0KPbe5lY-75WK/.

Gillessen, A., & Schmidt, H. (2020). Silymarin as supportive Treatment in liver Diseases: A Narrative review. *Advances in Therapy, 37*(4), 1279–1301. https://doi.org/10.1007/s12325-020-01251-y.

Godos, J., Caraci, F., Castellano, S., Currenti, W., Galvano, F., Ferri, R., & Grosso, G. (2020). Association Between Dietary Flavonoids Intake and Cognitive Function in an Italian Cohort. *Biomolecules, 10*(9), 1300. https://doi.org/10.3390/biom10091300.

GOODNET - GATEWAY TO DOING GOOD. (2022, September 20). *How to embrace getting older*. Goodnet. https://www.goodnet.org/articles/how-to-embrace-getting-older.

Griffiths, R. (2022). Healthy Habits through Self-Accountability. *Prime Women | an Online Magazine*. https://primewomen.com/wellness/health/finding-balance/healthy-habits-self-accountability/.

Hair, R., Sakaki, J., & Chun, O. K. (2021). Anthocyanins, microbiome and health benefits in aging. *Molecules, 26*(3), 537. https://doi.org/10.3390/molecules26030537.

Hand clenches chair yoga | Yoga sequences, benefits, variations, and Sanskrit Pronunciation | Tummee.com. (2018, March 12). Tummee.com. https://www.tummee.com/yoga-poses/hand-clenches-chair.

Harvard Health. (2022, August 25). *5 surprising benefits of walking*. https://www.health.harvard.edu/staying-healthy/5-surprising-benefits-of-walking#:~:text=Harvard%20researchers%20looked%20at%2032,genes%20were%20cut%20in%20half.

Hasanzade, F., Toliat, M., Emami, S. A., & Emamimoghaadam, Z. (2013). The effect of cinnamon on glucose of type II diabetes patients. *Journal of Traditional and Complementary Medicine, 3*(3), 171–174. https://doi.org/10.4103/2225-4110.114900.

Health habit accountability buddy. (2023, February 17). *Be Healthful*. https://www.behealthful.io/blog/health-habit-accountability-buddy.

Heaton, D. (2022). The paleo diet and its benefits to health and longevity. *Longevity.Technology Lifestyle | Health, Fitness & Technology*. https://longevity.technology/lifestyle/the-paleo-diet-and-its-benefits-to-health-and-longevity/.

Heel Raises chair yoga | Yoga sequences, benefits, variations, and Sanskrit Pronunciation | Tummee.com. (2018, July 26). Tummee.com. https://www.tummee.com/yoga-poses/heel-raises-chair.

Houghton, C. A. (2019). Sulforaphane: its "Coming of age" as a clinically relevant nutraceutical in the prevention and treatment of chronic disease. *Oxidative Medicine and Cellular Longevity, 2019*, 1–27. https://doi.org/10.1155/2019/2716870.

How to do Shoulder Shrugs. (n.d.). [Video]. skimble.com. https://www.skimble.com/exercises/1065-shoulder-shrugs-how-to-do-exercise.

Hu, Y., Hu, F. B., & Manson, J. E. (2019). Marine Omega-3 supplementation and cardiovascular Disease: An Updated Meta-Analysis of 13 randomized controlled trials involving 127 477 participants. *Journal of the American Heart Association, 8*(19). https://doi.org/10.1161/jaha.119.013543.

Hutchinson, A. N., Bergh, C., Krüger, K., Sűsserová, M., Allen, J. L., Améen, S., & Tingö, L. (2021). The effect of probiotics on health outcomes in the elderly: A Systematic Review of Randomized, Placebo-Controlled studies. *Microorganisms*, *9*(6), 1344. https://doi.org/10.3390/microorganisms9061344.

Julie. (2022, June 17). What is the Paleo Diet? A Straightforward Introduction for the Paleo-Curious. | Fox Hill Kitchens. *Fox Hill Kitchens*. https://foxhillkitchens.com/what-is-the-paleo-diet/.

Kan, J., Wu, F., Wang, F., Zheng, J., Cheng, J., Li, Y., Yang, Y., & Du, J. (2022). Phytonutrients: Sources, bioavailability, interaction with gut microbiota, and their impacts on human health. *Frontiers in Nutrition*, *9*. https://doi.org/10.3389/fnut.2022.960309.

Kandylis, P., & Kokkinomagoulos, E. (2020). Food Applications and Potential Health Benefits of Pomegranate and its Derivatives. *Foods*, *9*(2), 122. https://doi.org/10.3390/foods9020122.

Kang, J. H., Ascherio, A., & Grodstein, F. (2005). Fruit and vegetable consumption and cognitive decline in aging women. *Annals of Neurology*, *57*(5), 713–720. https://doi.org/10.1002/ana.20476.

Kavyani, Z., Musazadeh, V., Fathi, S., Faghfouri, A. H., Dehghan, P., & Sarmadi, B. (2022). Efficacy of the omega-3 fatty acids supplementation on inflammatory biomarkers: An umbrella meta-analysis. *International Immunopharmacology*, *111*, 109104. https://doi.org/10.1016/j.intimp.2022.109104.

Khalil, A. A., Rahman, U. U., Khan, M. R., Sahar, A., Mehmood, T., & Khan, M. (2017). Essential oil eugenol: sources, extraction techniques and nutraceutical perspectives. *RSC Advances*, *7*(52), 32669–32681. https://doi.org/10.1039/c7ra04803c.

Kim, D., Han, A., & Park, Y. (2021). Association of Dietary Total phytonutrient Capacity with Bone Mass and Osteoporosis Risk in Korean Women: Analysis of the Korea National Health and Nutrition Examination Survey 2008–2011. *Nutrients*, *13*(4), 1149. https://doi.org/10.3390/nu13041149.

Lally, P., Van Jaarsveld, C. H. M., Potts, H. W. W., & Wardle, J. (2009). How are habits formed: Modelling habit formation in the real world. *European Journal of Social Psychology*, *40*(6), 998–1009. https://doi.org/10.1002/ejsp.674.

Ledochowski, L., Ruedl, G., Taylor, A., & Kopp, M. (2015). Acute effects of brisk walking on sugary snack cravings in overweight people, affect and responses to a manipulated stress situation and to a sugary snack cue: a crossover study. *PLOS ONE*, *10*(3), e0119278. https://doi.org/10.1371/journal.pone.0119278.

Leow, S., Jackson, B., Alderson, J., Guelfi, K. J., & Dimmock, J. A. (2018). A role for exercise in attenuating unhealthy food consumption in response to stress. *Nutrients*, *10*(2), 176. https://doi.org/10.3390/nu10020176.

Levlanedev. (2021, October 21). *Wellness for Seniors: How to achieve your health goals - SearStone*. SearStone. https://searstone.com/wellness-for-seniors-how-to-achieve-your-health-goals/.

Liao, Y., Xie, B., Zhang, H., He, Q., Guo, L., Subramanieapillai, M., Fan, B., Lu, C., & McIntyre, R. S. (2019). Efficacy of omega-3 PUFAs in depression: A meta-analysis. *Translational Psychiatry*, *9*(1). https://doi.org/10.1038/s41398-019-0515-5.

Lindberg, S. (2020, January 10). *10 Shoulder mobility exercises and stretches*. Healthline. https://www.healthline.com/health/shoulder-mobility-exercises#stretches.

Liran. (2023, May 10). *12 Health benefits of paleo diets*. Popado – Life & Health Hub: Nourishing Body, Mind, and Soul With Food, Lifestyle, and Entertainment. https://popado.net/12-health-benefits-of-paleo-diets/?utm_source.

Liu, J., Zhou, H., Song, L., Yang, Z., Qu, M., Wang, J., & Shi, S. (2021). Anthocyanins: Promising Natural Products with Diverse Pharmacological Activities. *Molecules*, *26*(13), 3807. https://doi.org/10.3390/molecules26133807.

Lopresti, A. L., Smith, S. J., Jackson-Michel, S., & Fairchild, T. J. (2021). An Investigation into the Effects of a Curcumin Extract (Curcugen®) on Osteoarthritis Pain of the Knee: A Randomised, Double-Blind, Placebo-Controlled Study. *Nutrients*, *14*(1), 41. https://doi.org/10.3390/nu14010041.

MacKay, J. (2018). How to break bad habits (and build good ones at the same time). *RescueTime Blog*. https://blog.rescuetime.com/break-bad-habits/.

Manheimer, E., Van Zuuren, E., Fedorowicz, Z., & Pijl, H. (2015). Paleolithic nutrition for metabolic syndrome: systematic review and meta-analysis. *The American Journal of Clinical Nutrition, 102*(4), 922–932. https://doi.org/10.3945/ajcn.115.113613.

Marie, K. (2018). 10 reasons to embrace aging. *Slow Aging | Healthy Living, Healthy Aging.* https://slowaging.org/embrace-aging/

McFadden, B. J. (n.d.). The joy of ageing: why life just gets better after 60. *The Telegraph.* https://www.telegraph.co.uk/beauty/ageless-generation/how-to-embrace-ageing/.

McGinn, A. P., Kaplan, R. C., Verghese, J., Rosenbaum, D. M., Psaty, B. M., Baird, A. E., Lynch, J. K., Wolf, P. A., Kooperberg, C., Larson, J. C., & Wassertheil-Smoller, S. (2008). Walking speed and risk of incident Ischemic stroke among postmenopausal women. *Stroke, 39*(4), 1233–1239. https://doi.org/10.1161/strokeaha.107.500850.

McKay, D. L., Eliasziw, M., Chen, C. Y. O., & Blumberg, J. B. (2018). A Pecan-Rich diet improves cardiometabolic risk factors in overweight and obese adults: a randomized controlled trial. *Nutrients, 10*(3), 339. https://doi.org/10.3390/nu10030330.

Meydani, M., & Hasan, S. T. (2010). Dietary polyphenols and obesity. *Nutrients, 2*(7), 737–751. https://doi.org/10.3390/nu2070737.

Mineo, L. (2023, April 5). Over nearly 80 years, Harvard study has been showing how to live a healthy and happy life. *Harvard Gazette.* https://news.harvard.edu/gazette/story/2017/04/over-nearly-80-years-harvard-study-has-been-showing-how-to-live-a-healthy-and-happy-life/#:~:text=Close%20relationships%2C%20more%20than%20money,%2C%20IQ%2C%20or%20even%20genes.

Mohammadi, M., Mohammadi, H., Ghaedi, E., Ramezani-Jolfaie, N., & Salehi-Abargouei, A. (2019). Effects of paleolithic diet on glucose control in adults: a systematic review and meta-analysis of controlled clinical trials. *Journal of Nutrition and Food Security.* https://doi.org/10.18502/jnfs.v4i1.399.

Monjotin, N., Amiot, M., Fleurentin, J., Morel, J., & Raynal, S. (2022). Clinical evidence of the benefits of phytonutrients in human healthcare. *Nutrients, 14*(9), 1712. https://doi.org/10.3390/nu14091712.

Mountain Pose Chair One leg backlift Yoga (Tadasana chair Eka pada Backlift) | Yoga sequences, benefits, variations, and Sanskrit Pronunciation | Tummee.com. (2018, September 9). Tummee.com. https://www.tummee.com/yoga-poses/mountain-pose-chair-one-leg-backlift.

Mph, E. M. (2012, October 28). *Phytonutrients.* WebMD. https://www.webmd.com/diet/guide/phytonutrients-faq.

Mrowicka, M., Mrowicki, J., Kucharska, E., & Majsterek, I. (2022). Lutein and zeaxanthin and their roles in Age-Related Macular Degeneration—Neurodegenerative disease. *Nutrients, 14*(4), 827. https://doi.org/10.3390/nu14040827.

Murtagh, E. M., Murphy, M. H., & Boone-Heinonen, J. (2010). Walking: the first steps in cardiovascular disease prevention. *Current Opinion in Cardiology, 25*(5), 490–496. https://doi.org/10.1097/hco.0b013e32833ce972.

Nakhaee, S., Kooshki, A., Hormozi, A., Akbari, A., Mehrpour, O., & Farrokhfall, K. (2023). Cinnamon and cognitive function: a systematic review of preclinical and clinical studies. *Nutritional Neuroscience*, 1–15. https://doi.org/10.1080/1028415x.2023.2166436.

Neumann, R., Ahrens, K. F., Kollmann, B., Goldbach, N., Chmitorz, A., Weichert, D., Fiebach, C. J., Wessa, M., Kalisch, R., Lieb, K., Tüscher, O., Plichta, M. M., Reif, A., & Matura, S. (2021). The impact of physical fitness on resilience to modern life stress and the mediating role of general self-efficacy. *European Archives of Psychiatry and Clinical Neuroscience, 272*(4), 679–692. https://doi.org/10.1007/s00406-021-01338-9.

Newman, M. G., & Zainal, N. H. (2020). The value of maintaining social connections for mental health in older people. *Lancet Public Health, 5*(1), e12–e13. https://doi.org/10.1016/s2468-2667(19)30253-1.

O'Grady, T. (2021, December 13). Create affirmations to help you stick to your habit. *Medium.* https://medium.com/in-fitness-and-in-health/create-affirmations-to-help-you-stick-t%20o-your-habit-day-5-in-how-to-start-a-new-habit-262ece26d321.

Omura, J. D., Ussery, E. N., Loustalot, F., Fulton, J. E., & Carlson, S. A. (2019). Walking as an opportunity for cardiovascular disease prevention. *Preventing Chronic Disease, 16*. https://doi.org/10.5888/pcd16.180690.

Pan, L., Zhou, Y., Yin, H., Tian, J., Guo, Y., & Xie, X. (2021). Omega-3 Polyunsaturated Fatty Acids Can Reduce C-Reactive Protein in Patients with Cancer: A Systematic Review and Meta-Analysis of Randomized Controlled Trials. *Nutrition and Cancer*, 1–12. https://doi.org/10.1080/01 635581.2021.1931365.

Pang, Y., Bennett, D., Mafham, M., Lin, X., Chen, Z., Armitage, J., & Clarke, R. (2019). Vitamin D and calcium for the prevention of fracture. *JAMA Network Open*, 2(12), e1917789. https://doi.org/10.1001/jamanetworkopen.2019.17789.

Pap, N., Fidelis, M., Azevedo, L., Carmo, M. a. V. D., Wang, D., Mocan, A., Pereira, E. P. R., Xavier-Santos, D., Sant'Ana, A. S., Yang, B., & Granato, D. (2021). Berry polyphenols and human health: evidence of phytonutrient, anti-inflammatory, microbiota modulation, and cell-protecting effects. *Current Opinion in Food Science*, 42, 167–186. https://doi.org/10.1016/j.cofs.2021.06.003.

Parker, S. (2021). The science of habits. *Knowable Magazine*. https://doi.org/10.1146/knowable-071521-1.

Pelley, V. (2023, July 20). Your Guide To The Best Anti-Aging Supplements. *Forbes Health*. https://www.forbes.com/health/healthy-aging/best-anti-aging-supplements/.

Pinckard, K. M., Baskin, K. K., & Stanford, K. I. (2019). Effects of exercise to improve cardiovascular health. *Frontiers in Cardiovascular Medicine*, 6. https://doi.org/10.3389/fcvm.2019.00069.

Pinheiro, M. B., Oliveira, J. S., Bauman, A., Fairhall, N., Kwok, W., & Sherrington, C. (2020). Evidence on physical activity and osteoporosis prevention for people aged 65+ years: a systematic review to inform the WHO guidelines on physical activity and sedentary behaviour. *International Journal of Behavioral Nutrition and Physical Activity*, 17(1). https://doi.org/10.1186/s12966-020-01040-4.

Poulose, S. M., Miller, M. G., & Shukitt-Hale, B. (2014). Role of Walnuts in Maintaining Brain Health with Age. *Journal of Nutrition*, 144(4), 561S-566S. https://doi.org/10.3945/jn.113.184838.

Rabbitt, M. (2023, February 6). 7 exercises that Instantly Un-Hunch your shoulders. *Prevention*. https://www.prevention.com/fitness/g20489329/7-exercises-that-instantly-un-hunch-yourshoulders/.

Rattanawiwatpong, P., Wanitphakdeedecha, R., Bumrungpert, A., & Maiprasert, M. (2020). Anti-aging and brightening effects of a topical treatment containing vitamin C, vitamin E, and raspberry leaf cell culture extract: A split-face, randomized controlled trial. *Journal of Cosmetic Dermatology, 19*(3), 671–676. https://doi.org/10.1111/jocd.13305.

Rd, R. a. M. (2021, September 7). *A definitive guide to supplements for healthy aging.* Healthline. https://www.healthline.com/nutrition/a-definitive-guide-to-supplements-for-healthy-aging.

Rees, A., Dodd, G. D., & Spencer, J. P. (2018). The effects of flavonoids on cardiovascular health: A review of human intervention trials and implications for cerebrovascular function. *Nutrients, 10*(12), 1852. https://doi.org/10.3390/nu10121852.

Reid, T. (2014, September 29). Form better habits by making them more convenient. *Lifehacker.* https://lifehacker.com/form-better-habits-by-making-them-more-convenient-1640358351.

Resource, F. (2023, June 28). Why is Independence Important to Seniors? | Family Resource Home Care. *Family Resource Home Care.* https://www.familyresourcehomecare.com/why-is-independence-important-to-seniors/.

Robinson, L. (2023). How to start exercising and stick to it. *HelpGuide.org.* https://www.helpguide.org/articles/healthy-living/how-to-start-exercising-and-stick-to-it.htm.

Rodríguez-García, C., Sánchez-Quesada, C., Toledo, E., Delgado-Rodríguez, M., & Gaforio, J. J. (2019). Naturally Lignan-Rich foods: a dietary tool for health promotion? *Molecules, 24*(5), 917. https://doi.org/10.3390/molecules24050917.

Rubin, G. (n.d.). *How To Keep A Habit Lapse From Turning Into A Relapse.* Next Big Idea Club. https://nextbigideaclub.com/magazine/video-for-habits-the-strategy-of-safeguards/6458/.

Rubin, G. (2015). One Of The Most Important Strategies For Changing Your Habits. *Fast Company.* https://www.fastcompany.com/3043658/why-you-should-schedule-habit-changes-in-the-morning.

Scheduling | Lunatask. (n.d.). Lunatask. https://lunatask.app/docs/features/habits/scheduling

Seated Cactus arms Flow Chair yoga | Yoga sequences, benefits, variations, and Sanskrit Pronunciation | Tummee.com. (2019, February 12). Tummee.com. https://www.tummee.com/yoga-poses/seated-cactus-arms-flow-chair.

Seaver, M. (2023, March 31). Habit Stacking Is the Easiest Way to Make New Habits Last—Here's How It Works. *Real Simple.* https://www.real-simple.com/work-life/life-strategies/inspiration-motivation/habit-stack-ing.

Senior Services of America. (2023, July 12). *Chair Exercises for Seniors - Senior Services of America.* https://seniorservicesofamerica.com/blog/chair-ex-ercises-for-seniors/.

Shoulder Pendulum Exercises Chair Yoga | Yoga Sequences, Benefits, Variations, and Sanskrit Pronunciation | Tummee.com. (2020, July 1). Tummee.com. https://www.tummee.com/yoga-poses/shoulder-pendulum-exercises-chair.

Si, H., & Liu, D. (2014). Dietary antiaging phytochemicals and mechanisms associated with prolonged survival. *Journal of Nutritional Biochemistry, 25*(6), 581–591. https://doi.org/10.1016/j.jnutbio.2014.02.001.

Sloan, E., & Sloan, E. (2022). 'Habit stacking' is the simple mind trick for making a new routine or ritual stick. *Well+Good.* https://www.welland-good.com/habit-stacking/.

Stoewen, D. L. (2017). Dimensions of wellness: Change your habits, change your life. *PubMed, 58*(8), 861–862. https://pubmed.ncbi.nlm.nih.gov/28761196.

Story, E. N., Kopec, R. E., Schwartz, S. J., & Harris, G. K. (2010). An up-date on the health effects of tomato lycopene. *Annual Review of Food Science and Technology, 1*(1), 189–210. https://doi.org/10.1146/annurev.food.102308.124120.

Tan, B. L., & Norhaizan, M. E. (2019). Carotenoids: How effective are they to prevent Age-Related Diseases? *Molecules, 24*(9), 1801. https://doi.org/10.3390/molecules24091801.

Teeter. (2021). 10 simple ways to sneak more exercise into your daily rou-tine. *Teeter.com.* https://teeter.com/blog/simple-exercise-daily-routine/.

The House of Wellness. (2022, June 3). *Embrace ageing: How to accept getting older as a natural part of life.* The House of Wellness. https://www.hou-seofwellness.com.au/wellbeing/advice/how-to-embrace-ageing.

The Paleo Diet — An Introduction | The Source Bulk Foods. (2022, April 4). The Source Bulk Foods. https://thesourcebulkfoods.com.au/blog/the-paleo-diet-an-introduction/.

Therapy Brands. (2023, March 29). *How to maintain healthy habits during times of High stress | Therapy brands.* https://therapybrands.com/blog/how-to-maintain-healthy-habits-during-times-of-high-stress/.

Tree Pose Holding onto chair yoga (Vrksasana holding onto chair) | yoga sequences, benefits, variations, and Sanskrit pronunciation | Tummee.com. (2018, June 20). Tummee.com. https://www.tummee.com/yoga-poses/tree-pose-holding-onto-chair.

Tummee yoga poses half wide legged forward fold pose hands back of chair - Google Search. (n.d.). https://www.tummee.com/yoga-poses/half-wide-legged-forward-fold-pose-hands-back-ofchair.

Turner-McGrievy, G., Mandes, T., & Crimarco, A. (2017). A plant-based diet for overweight and obesity prevention and treatment. *PubMed, 14*(5), 369–374. https://doi.org/10.11909/j.issn.1671-5411.2017.05.002.

Ullah, A., Munir, S., Badshah, S. L., Khan, N., Ghani, L., Poulson, B. G., & Emwas, A. (2020). Important flavonoids and their role as a therapeutic agent. *Molecules, 25*(22), 5243. https://doi.org/10.3390/molecules25225243.

Vambheim, S. M., Kyllo, T. M., Hegland, S., & Bystad, M. (2021). Relaxation techniques as an intervention for chronic pain: A systematic review of randomized controlled trials. *Heliyon, 7*(8), e07837. https://doi.org/10.1016/j.heliyon.2021.e07837.

Voutilainen, S., Nurmi, T., Mursu, J., & Rissanen, T. H. (2006). Carotenoids and cardiovascular health. *The American Journal of Clinical Nutrition, 83*(6), 1265–1271. https://doi.org/10.1093/ajcn/83.6.1265.

Wallace, T. C. (2011). Anthocyanins in cardiovascular disease. *Advances in Nutrition, 2*(1), 1–7. https://doi.org/10.3945/an.110.000042.

Why am I craving sweets: The Science behind sugar. (n.d.). Thorne. https://www.thorne.com/take-5-daily/article/the-science-behind-sugar-cravings.

Wilson, J. (2017). How Convenience Can Help Us Establish Good Habits — parent|re.mix. *Parent|re.mix.* https://www.parentremix.com/personal-effectiveness/2017/3/12/convenience-is-good-and-bad.

Wisbey, S. (2023). 7 tips for choosing a quality supplement. *BetterYou*. https://betteryou.com/blogs/product-guides/how-to-choose-the-best-supplements.

Wu, J., Cho, E., Willett, W. C., Sastry, S. M., & Schaumberg, D. A. (2015). Intakes of lutein, zeaxanthin, and other carotenoids and Age-Related macular degeneration during 2 decades of prospective follow-up. *JAMA Ophthalmology*, *133*(12), 1415. https://doi.org/10.1001/jamaophthalmol.2015.3590.

YouBetterSelf.com. (2023, March 23). Holistic Wellness for Seniors At Home: A Path to Healthy Living. *Unlock Your Potential: Path to Self-Improvement*. https://www.youbetterself.com/holistic-wellness-for-seniors-at-home/.

Zhan, L., Guo, D., Chen, G., & Yang, J. (2018). Effects of repetition learning on associative recognition over time: role of the hippocampus and prefrontal cortex. *Frontiers in Human Neuroscience*, *12*. https://doi.org/10.3389/fnhum.2018.00277.

Printed in Great Britain
by Amazon

45843946R00092